HAMLET

HARCOURT SHAKESPEARE

HAMLET

Second Edition

Series Editor: Ken Roy

edited by
Marilyn Eisenstat

NELSON

NELSON

National Library of Canada Cataloguing in Publication Data

Shakespeare, William, 1564–1616
    Harcourt Shakespeare : Hamlet / edited by Marilyn Eisenstat.—
2nd ed.

ISBN 0-7747-1484-0

    I. Eisenstat, Marilyn II. Title.

PR2807.A2E27 2003
    822.3'3   C2003-904192-1

Harcourt Shakespeare: Series Editor, Ken Roy

Project Manager: Terry-Lee Wheelband
Developmental Editor: Jane A. Clark
Production Editor: Shefali Mehta
Production Coordinators: Kimberly Sullivan and David Ward
Copy Editor: Eliza Marciniak
Page Composition: Rachel Rosen
Cover and Text Illustrations: Marika and Laszlo Gal
Printing and Binding: Friesens

Nelson Education Ltd.
1120 Birchmount Road
Toronto, Ontario M1K 5G4
1-800-668-0671
nelson.com

Printed in Canada
24 25 26   24 23 22

To the Reader

You are probably already familiar with some elements of
Hamlet—the famous soliloquy that begins with the line,
"To be, or not to be: that is the question," for example,
or the image of Hamlet holding a skull saying, "Alas,
poor Yorick! I knew him." As you begin to read the play,
you will also recognize many of the plot elements, as
they are often found in movies and television dramas
today. For example, murder, betrayal, friendship,
destroyed love, and revenge are all part of *Hamlet*. As
well, when you become familiar with Hamlet's complex,
multifaceted character, you may find yourself relating
parts of his personality to your own.

This text provides you with an approach to *Hamlet*
that aims both to help and to challenge you. Before
reading each scene, you will have the opportunity to
explore ideas or personal experiences similar to those
you will read about. The short scene summaries given
at the beginning of each scene will help you to
understand plot developments.

After each scene there are activities that invite you to
respond in several ways to ideas and problems raised
in the scene. Some involve group work and others
require you to work individually. There is a wide variety
of activities, ranging from private journal responses to
group performances, which will encourage you to
respond to ideas in different ways, and deepen your
understanding of the play.

Now that you have an idea how this play will be
presented, you are ready to begin your exploration of
Hamlet.

Getting Started

Hamlet is based on an old story that Shakespeare
adapted. It belongs to a tradition of revenge tragedies that

were familiar to Elizabethan audiences. Tales of revenge have always been popular, and Shakespeare enriched this story with many other themes and subplots that still have relevance today.

1. Four story outlines are given below. All of these stories are found in *Hamlet*. As you read through the outlines, consider whether any of these situations are familiar to you from your own experience, or from books, television, or movies.

   a) *Revenge*

   The main character is a sensitive young man who is recovering from the death of his father when he learns that someone in his own family murdered his father. There is no conclusive proof, but the main character decides to take revenge on the murderer.

   b) *Rejected Love*

   The main character (male) is in love. His girlfriend's father has forbidden her to see the young man again. She rejects the main character's advances and returns his gifts. The girlfriend and the young man are both very upset, but cope with the separation differently.

   c) *Madness*

   The main character is a young man whose comfortable life has suddenly been shattered by a violent event. He reacts to the shock by isolating himself from family and friends and either goes mad or pretends to go mad. All his relationships, including a love relationship, change as a result.

   d) *Family Pressures*

   After a young man's father dies, his mother quickly remarries someone the young man hates. The young man is disgusted by the change he observes in his mother's behaviour. He would like to escape, but his stepfather wants him to remain at home and live with them.

   In groups of three or four people, choose one of the four stories. What conflicts or themes could develop in that story? Share your findings with the class.

2. Start keeping a personal journal in which you can record your reactions both to the play itself and discussions about it. Reflect on whether any of the ideas your group discussed or that other groups presented to the class related to activity 1 have any relevance to your own life or to movies or television shows you have seen recently.

Keeping a journal

Your journal may be used for many different kinds of reflection as you study Hamlet. *Some of your writing will be confidential, but you may want to share some parts with your classmates and/or teacher. Decide with your teacher how to set up your journal to ensure your privacy. Using the date and a heading for each entry will help you to keep track of your developing experience of the play.*

3. *Hamlet* raises many questions that you may recognize from your own life. Thinking beforehand about some of these issues will make your experience of the play more interesting and rewarding. Discuss some of the following questions in your group. Record in your journal any ideas you find interesting or thought-provoking. When you begin to read and discuss the play, you may want to refer to these notes and keep track of any changes in your opinions, or any surprises you find.

   a) We have all procrastinated about something important that we had to do, sometimes disappointing other people and often disappointing ourselves. Why do we procrastinate?

   b) Most people have purposely "played the fool" at some time. Why do people do this? If a person for some reason plays the fool or pretends to be disturbed for a long time, do you think the person eventually can become truly disturbed?

   c) Isolation and loneliness are feelings common to most people at one time or another. Sometimes external circumstances create this situation, and sometimes people deliberately withdraw from those around them. What can friends or relatives do when someone has purposely withdrawn and chosen to be alone with his or her problems?

d) Disillusion is a common experience of growing up. We find that people in the adult world whom we once idealized are less than ideal, and that situations we considered innocent are actually corrupt. How do young people encountering the "real world" for the first time handle these discoveries?

e) In Shakespeare's time, insane people were regarded as sources of entertainment. What is our society's attitude toward mental illness?

f) What is the difference between "taking revenge" and "getting justice"?

g) Privacy is highly valued in our society. How would you feel if you found out that you were "under surveillance" at school, at your job, at home, or among friends because of some change in your behaviour?

Having thought about this wide range of topics, you are ready to explore *Hamlet*.

Dramatis Personae
(Characters in the Play)

Claudius, King of Denmark
Hamlet, son to the late and nephew to the present King
Polonius, Lord Chamberlain
Horatio, friend to Hamlet
Laertes, son to Polonius
Voltimand
Cornelius
Rosencrantz ⎫ courtiers
Guildenstern ⎬
Osric
A Gentleman
A Priest
Marcellus ⎫ officers
Bernardo ⎬
Francisco, a soldier
Reynaldo, servant to Polonius
Players
Two clowns, grave-diggers
A Captain
English Ambassadors
Fortinbras, Prince of Norway
Gertrude, Queen of Denmark and mother to Hamlet
Ophelia, daughter to Polonius
Lords, Ladies, Officers, Soldiers, Players, Sailors,
    Messengers, and other Attendants
Ghost of Hamlet's father

Scene: Elsinore

Act 1, Scene 1

In this scene . . .

The play begins on the outer ramparts of the King's palace in Elsinore, the capital of Old Denmark. It is midnight. Bernardo has come to take over guard duty from Francisco. As they exchange greetings, Marcellus, another guard, approaches. He has brought along Horatio, a scholar, to verify the appearance of the ghost of old King Hamlet, who died recently. The Ghost appears twice, and Horatio, who was skeptical at first, is convinced of its presence. He promises to report the Ghost's appearance to his friend, Prince Hamlet, the son of the dead king.

Stage direction

platform: the ramparts or walls, where soldiers would keep watch

2   *unfold yourself:* identify yourself

3   *Long live the king:* the watchword for the night

6   *carefully:* precisely

12   *rivals:* partners

15   *the Dane:* King of Denmark

16   *Give you good night:* May God give you a good night.

Act 1, Scene 1

*Elsinore. A platform before
the castle.*

*Francisco on his post. Enter
to him Bernardo*

Bernardo: Who's there?
Francisco: Nay, answer me: stand, and unfold yourself.
Bernardo: Long live the king!
Francisco: Bernardo?
Bernardo: He. 5
Francisco: You come most carefully upon your hour.
Bernardo: 'Tis now struck twelve; get thee to bed, Francisco.
Francisco: For this relief much thanks: 'tis bitter cold,
    And I am sick at heart.
Bernardo: Have you had quiet guard?
Francisco: Not a mouse stirring. 10
Bernardo: Well, good night.
    If you do meet Horatio and Marcellus,
    The rivals of my watch, bid them make haste.
Francisco: I think I hear them. Stand, ho! who is there?

[*Enter Horatio and Marcellus.*]

Horatio: Friends to this ground.
Marcellus: And liegemen to the Dane. 15
Francisco: Give you good night.
Marcellus: O, farewell, honest soldier:
    Who hath relieved you?
Francisco: Bernardo hath my place.
    Give you good night.   [*Exit Francisco.*]
Marcellus: Holla! Bernardo!
Bernardo: Say,
    What, is Horatio there?

19	*a piece of him:* Different interpretations of this phrase have been given. Some people think Horatio means he is present in body but not in spirit (he wishes he were somewhere else). Others think he is referring to the cold, and still others that he is offering his hand to Bernardo. At any rate, Horatio seems to be making light of the situation.
23	*fantasy:* imagination
28	*apparition:* ghost
29	*He may approve our eyes:* He may confirm with his own eyes what we have seen.
31	*assail your ears:* force you to listen
36	*the pole:* the North Star, also known as the pole star
42	*Thou art a scholar:* Being an educated man, Horatio will know how to speak to the Ghost, perhaps in Latin.
44	*harrows:* stirs. A harrow is a heavy farm implement used to turn the soil.
45	*It would . . . to:* It was believed ghosts could not speak until they were spoken to first.
48	*buried Denmark:* the dead King of Denmark
49	*sometimes:* formerly

Horatio: A piece of him.
Bernardo: Welcome, Horatio; welcome, good Marcellus.   20
Marcellus: What, has this thing appear'd again tonight?
Bernardo: I have seen nothing.
Marcellus: Horatio says 'tis but our fantasy,
   And will not let belief take hold of him
   Touching this dreaded sight, twice seen of us: 25
   Therefore I have entreated him along
   With us to watch the minutes of this night;
   That if again this apparition come,
   He may approve our eyes and speak to it.
Horatio: Tush! tush! 'twill not appear.
Bernardo: Sit down a while;   30
   And let us once again assail your ears,
   That are so fortified against our story,
   What we two nights have seen.
Horatio: Well, sit we down,
   And let us hear Bernardo speak of this.
Bernardo: Last night of all,   35
   When yond same star that's westward from the pole
   Had made his course to illume that part of heaven
   Where now it burns, Marcellus and myself,
   The bell then beating one,—
Marcellus: Peace! break thee off; look, where it comes again!   40

   [Enter Ghost.]

Bernardo: In the same figure, like the king that's dead.
Marcellus: Thou art a scholar; speak to it, Horatio.
Bernardo: Looks it not like the king? mark it, Horatio.
Horatio: Most like: it harrows me with fear and wonder.
Bernardo: It would be spoke to.
Marcellus: Question it, Horatio.   45
Horatio: What art thou, that usurp'st this time of night,
   Together with that fair and warlike form
   In which the majesty of buried Denmark
   Did sometimes march? by heaven I charge thee, speak.
Marcellus: It is offended.
Bernardo: See, it stalks away.   50
Horatio: Stay! speak! speak! I charge thee, speak!
                    [Exit Ghost.]

56-58	*I might not . . . own eyes:* I could not believe this without the undeniable evidence of my senses.
61	*Norway:* King of Norway
62	*parle:* argument
63	*sledded Polack:* The Poles travelled in sleds.
65	*jump:* exactly
66	*martial stalk:* walking like a soldier
67	*thought:* intention
68	*in the gross . . . opinion:* as far as I can understand it
69	*This bodes . . . state:* This is a sign of some upheaval in Denmark.
71-79	Marcellus is referring to intense preparations for war being carried out in Denmark.
73	*cast:* casting
74	*foreign mart:* buying from foreign countries
75	*impress:* forced service
77	*toward:* under way
83	*emulate:* jealous
86-95	The two kings staked portions of their territories on the result of the combat, and Hamlet won.

Marcellus: 'Tis gone, and will not answer.
Bernardo: How now, Horatio! you tremble, and look pale:
    Is not this something more than fantasy?
    What think you on't?   55
Horatio: Before my God, I might not this believe,
    Without the sensible and true avouch
    Of mine own eyes.
Marcellus: Is it not like the king?
Horatio: As thou art to thyself:
    Such was the very armour he had on   60
    When he the ambitious Norway combated;
    So frown'd he once, when, in an angry parle,
    He smote the sledded Polack on the ice.
    'Tis strange.
Marcellus: Thus twice before, and jump at this dead hour,   65
    With martial stalk hath he gone by our watch.
Horatio: In what particular thought to work I know not;
    But, in the gross and scope of my opinion,
    This bodes some strange eruption to our state.
Marcellus: Good now, sit down, and tell me, he that knows,   70
    Why this same strict and most observant watch
    So nightly toils the subject of the land,
    And why such daily cast of brazen cannon,
    And foreign mart for implements of war:
    Why such impress of shipwrights, whose sore task   75
    Does not divide the Sunday from the week.
    What might be toward, that this sweaty haste
    Doth make the night joint-labourer with the day:
    Who is't that can inform me?
Horatio: That can I:
    At least the whisper goes so. Our last king,   80
    Whose image even but now appear'd to us,
    Was, as you know, by Fortinbras of Norway,
    Thereto prick'd on by a most emulate pride,
    Dared to the combat; in which our valiant Hamlet—
    For so this side of our known world esteem'd him—   85
    Did slay this Fortinbras; who, by a seal'd compact,
    Well ratified by law and heraldry,
    Did forfeit, with his life, all those his lands
    Which he stood seized of, to the conqueror:

90-91	*a moiety . . . our king:* A sufficient portion was pledged by our king.
91	*had return'd:* would have returned
96	*Of unimproved metal:* impetuous, not yet seasoned by experience
97	*skirts:* outlying regions (outskirts)
98	*Shark'd up:* gathered together; *lawless resolutes:* desperadoes
99	*For food and diet:* The soldiers' only payment was food.
99-100	*some enterprise . . . stomach in't:* an adventure requiring courage
103	*terms compulsatory:* conditions forced on us
106	*head:* source
107	*romage:* disturbance, turmoil
109	*Well may it sort:* it may be appropriate; *portentous:* fatal, ominous
112	*mote:* speck of dust. (The military situation is like a speck of dust in the eye—very bothersome and disruptive.)
114-125	Horatio is giving a list of unnatural occurrences that happened in Rome prior to Julius Caesar's assassination.
115	*sheeted:* wrapped in shrouds (sometimes called "winding sheets")
118	*Disasters in the sun:* possibly eclipses, which were thought to be evil omens; *moist star:* moon, which influences the tides
121	*precurse:* warnings
122	*harbingers:* forerunners
123	*omen:* dreaded event
125	*climatures:* territories
127	*cross:* make the sign of the cross, or cross the path of the Ghost. (If he crosses the Ghost's path, he will be under its influence); *blast:* destroy

14

Against the which, a moiety competent   90
Was gaged by our king; which had return'd
To the inheritance of Fortinbras,
Had he been vanquisher; as, by the same covenant
And carriage of the article design'd,
His fell to Hamlet. Now, sir, young Fortinbras,   95
Of unimproved metal, hot and full,
Hath in the skirts of Norway, here and there
Shark'd up a list of lawless resolutes,
For food and diet, to some enterprise
That hath a stomach in't: which is no other—   100
And it doth well appear unto our state—
But to recover of us, by strong hand
And terms compulsatory, those 'foresaid lands
So by his father lost: and this, I take it,
Is the main motive of our preparations,   105
The source of this our watch and the chief head
Of this post-haste and romage in the land.
Bernardo: I think it be no other, but e'en so
    Well may it sort, that this portentous figure
    Comes armed through our watch, so like the king   110
    That was and is the question of these wars.
Horatio: A mote it is to trouble the mind's eye.
    In the most high and palmy state of Rome,
    A little ere the mightiest Julius fell,
    The graves stood tenantless, and the sheeted dead   115
    Did squeak and gibber in the Roman streets:
    As stars with trains of fire and dews of blood,
    Disasters in the sun; and the moist star,
    Upon whose influence Neptune's empire stands,
    Was sick almost to doomsday with eclipse: 120
    And even the like precurse of fierce events,
    As harbingers preceding still the fates
    And prologue to the omen coming on,
    Have heaven and earth together demonstrated
    Unto our climatures and countrymen.   125

[Re-enter Ghost.]

But soft, behold! lo, where it comes again!
I'll cross it, though it blast me. Stay, illusion!

133   *art privy to:* have secret information about

134   *happily:* by luck

140   *partizan:* long-handled battle-axe

147-157   It was a common belief that when the cock crows at day-break, wandering spirits must return to their proper places. In agricultural societies, this encouraged farmers to go to work more cheerfully.

148   *started:* was startled, jumped guiltily

152   *god of day:* Apollo

154   *extravagant and erring spirit:* wandering spirit, one that has escaped its confines

155   *confine:* proper dwelling place

156   *probation:* proof

158   *'gainst:* in preparation for

If thou hast any sound, or use of voice,
Speak to me:
If there be any good thing to be done,   130
That may to thee do ease and grace to me,
Speak to me:
If thou art privy to thy country's fate,
Which, happily, foreknowing may avoid,
O, speak!   135
Or, if thou hast uphoarded in thy life
Extorted treasure in the womb of earth,
For which, they say, you spirits oft walk in death,
                  [*Cock crows.*]
Speak of it: stay, and speak! Stop it, Marcellus.
Marcellus: Shall I strike at it with my partizan?   140
Horatio: Do, if it will not stand.
Bernardo: 'Tis here!
Horatio: 'Tis here!
Marcellus: 'Tis gone!   [*Exit Ghost.*]
We do it wrong, being so majestical,
To offer it the show of violence;
For it is, as the air, invulnerable,   145
And our vain blows malicious mockery.
Bernardo: It was about to speak when the cock crew.
Horatio: And then it started like a guilty thing
Upon a fearful summons. I have heard,
The cock, that is the trumpet to the morn,   150
Doth with his lofty and shrill-sounding throat
Awake the god of day; and at his warning,
Whether in sea or fire, in earth or air,
The extravagant and erring spirit hies
To his confine: and of the truth herein   155
This present object made probation.
Marcellus: It faded on the crowing of the cock.
Some say, that ever 'gainst that season comes
Wherein our Saviour's birth is celebrated,
The bird of dawning singeth all night long: 160
And then, they say, no spirit dare stir abroad;
The nights are wholesome; then no planets strike,
No fairy takes, nor witch hath power to charm,
So hallow'd and so gracious is the time.

166-167   *the morn . . . clad:* The dawn is cloudy or misty; *russet* could mean brown or grey in colour. Either colour suggests the beginning of daylight.

173   *loves:* these men are Hamlet's personal friends

Horatio: So have I heard, and do in part believe it.   165
    But look, the morn, in russet mantle clad,
    Walks o'er the dew of yon high eastern hill:
    Break we our watch up; and, by my advice,
    Let us impart what we have seen to-night
    Unto young Hamlet: for, upon my life,   170
    This spirit, dumb to us, will speak to him;
    Do you consent we shall acquaint him with it,
    As needful in our loves, fitting our duty?
Marcellus: Let's do't, I pray: and I this morning know
    Where we shall find him most conveniently.   175

                         [*Exeunt.*]

Act 1, Scene 1: Activities

1. *Hamlet* was originally performed at London's Globe Theatre. It was performed without scenery, in the natural afternoon light, in front of a noisy, boisterous audience. Shakespeare had to capture the audience's attention and establish the mood immediately.

   - In your group, take a few minutes to practise the first 14 lines of the play. With your voices only, try to capture the atmosphere of the cold and the tension. Differentiate between Francisco's weariness and Bernardo's anticipation of his watch.

   - Perform the dialogue for another group.

   With your group, discuss whether your performance achieved the effects you were hoping to produce.

2. In the role of a modern journalist, prepare a newspaper report describing Denmark's ongoing defence preparations and explaining the reasons for them. Keep in mind the following as you prepare your report:

   - Capture your reader's attention at the beginning of your story. Your first sentence or "lead" must be interesting and lively.

   - The most important information should appear at the beginning of your news story (who, what, when, where, why, and how).

   - Opinions can be quoted by attributing them to "unnamed palace sources."

   - Language should be simple and understandable.

   - The ending should create interest or questions about the future.

   Exchange your work with a classmate and discuss differences between the reports.

3. In your journal, write a detailed description of the Ghost in your own words, based on the observations of Bernardo and Horatio. Why do you think there has always been such a strong interest in ghosts?

4. In your group, discuss why you think the ghost of the former king has appeared. Collect hints from this scene that might support your guesses. Report your strongest guess, and your evidence, to the class.

5. Choose the lines that most vividly reveal Horatio's character to you, and discuss these lines with a partner. Does he remind you of anyone you know? Why do you think Marcellus confided in Horatio and not someone else?

6. Watch this scene on a video or DVD. During your viewing or immediately after, make notes about the following:

   • What is the most memorable part of this scene?

   • How did the director create the mood of the scene?

   In your journal, comment on any changes to this scene that you would recommend to the director. You might choose to discuss these with your group or with the class.

For the next scene . . .

In your journal, write about a time when your parents or other authority figures asked you to make a major change in specific plans you had made. What thoughts went through your mind? How did you respond to the request?

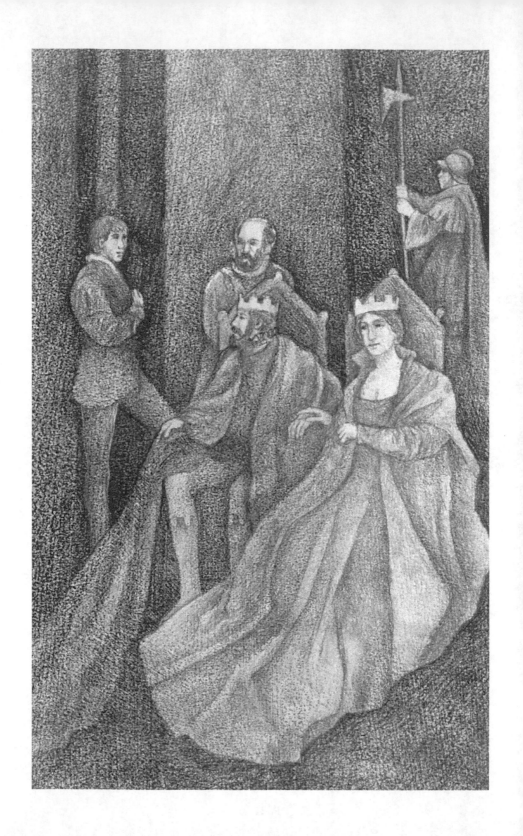

Act 1, Scene 2

In this scene . . .

This court scene is a strong contrast to the bleak first scene of the play. Claudius, brother to the dead King Hamlet, is now king. Soon after old Hamlet's death, Claudius married the King's widow, Queen Gertrude, who is Hamlet's mother. Claudius, who is conducting court business for the first time, is thinking about the impression he will make. He has planned each word and action carefully. He transacts several pieces of business, which move the action of the play forward and smooth over the awkwardness of his hasty marriage and accession to the throne. Claudius takes measures to prevent war against Norway. He grants permission to Laertes, son of the Lord Chamberlain Polonius, to return to France. Finally, he urges the depressed Prince Hamlet to stay in Denmark rather than return to university in Wittenberg. In the last part of the scene, Hamlet is alone on stage in the first of several soliloquies he speaks in the play. These soliloquies, which in some ways are like a personal journal, give us an opportunity to see the workings of Hamlet's mind; we not only learn what he is thinking, but we also learn *how* he thinks. Here, he expresses his depression and anger about his mother's remarriage. After the soliloquy, Horatio, Marcellus, and Bernardo arrive to tell Hamlet about his father's ghost. Hamlet promises to join them on the castle platform that night.

2   *green:* fresh

3-4   *our whole kingdom . . . woe:* for everyone in our kingdom to
         be united in sorrow

5   *discretion:* prudence; *nature:* feeling

8   *sometime sister:* former sister-in-law

9   *jointress:* partner

10   *defeated:* disfigured, marred

11   *With one . . . eye:* This resembles the proverbial phrase, "To
         laugh with one eye and cry with the other."

13   *dole:* grief

14   *barr'd:* excluded

15-16   *gone . . . along:* approved of what was happening

18   *supposal:* estimation

20   *out of frame:* out of order

21   *Colleagued:* adding to

23   *Importing:* concerning

28   *Norway:* King of Norway

Scene 2

A room of state in the castle.

Flourish. Enter the King, Queen,
Hamlet, Polonius, Laertes,
Voltimand, Cornelius, Lords, and
Attendants.

King: Though yet of Hamlet our dear brother's death
    The memory be green, and that it us befitted
    To bear our hearts in grief and our whole kingdom
    To be contracted in one brow of woe,
    Yet so far hath discretion fought with nature   5
    That we with wisest sorrow think on him,
    Together with remembrance of ourselves.
    Therefore our sometime sister, now our queen,
    The imperial jointress of this warlike state,
    Have we, as 'twere with a defeated joy,—   10
    With one auspicious and a dropping eye,
    With mirth in funeral and with dirge in marriage,
    In equal scale weighing delight and dole,—
    Taken to wife: nor have we herein barr'd
    Your better wisdoms, which have freely gone   15
    With this affair along. For all, our thanks.
    Now follows that you know, young Fortinbras,
    Holding a weak supposal of our worth,
    Or thinking, by our late dear brother's death
    Our state to be disjoint and out of frame,   20
    Colleagued with the dream of his advantage,
    He hath not fail'd to pester us with message,
    Importing the surrender of those lands
    Lost by his father, with all bonds of law,
    To our most valiant brother. So much for him.   25
    Now for ourself, and for this time of meeting:
    Thus much the business is: we have here writ
    To Norway, uncle of young Fortinbras,—

31	*gait:* progress

38	*delated articles:* detailed account of the situation
39	*let your haste commend your duty:* depart quickly without standing on ceremony

41	*nothing:* not at all

43	*suit:* request
44	*of reason:* of anything reasonable
45	*lose your voice:* ask in vain

47	*native:* naturally related to
47-49	Claudius is referring to his close relationship with Laertes' father, Polonius, who may have aided Claudius in becoming King after old King Hamlet's death.

51	*leave and favour:* permission

56	*leave and pardon:* permission to leave

62	*Take thy fair hour:* Feel free to leave whenever you wish.

64	*cousin:* nephew. The word "cousin" was used to refer to an uncle, aunt, niece, nephew or cousin.

Who, impotent and bed-rid, scarcely hears
Of this his nephew's purpose,—to suppress   30
His further gait herein; in that the levies,
The lists, and full proportions, are all made
Out of his subject: and we here despatch
You, good Cornelius, and you, Voltimand,
For bearing of this greeting to old Norway,   35
Giving to you no further personal power
To business with the king, more than the scope
Of these delated articles allow.
Farewell, and let your haste commend your duty.
Cornelius, Voltimand: In that and all things will we show
    our duty.   40
King: We doubt it nothing; heartily farewell.
                [*Exeunt Voltimand and Cornelius.*]
And now, Laertes, what's the news with you?
You told us of some suit: what is't, Laertes?
You cannot speak of reason to the Dane,
And lose your voice: what wouldst thou beg, Laertes,   45
That shall not be my offer, not thy asking?
The head is not more native to the heart,
The hand more instrumental to the mouth,
Than is the throne of Denmark to thy father.
What wouldst thou have, Laertes?
Laertes: My dread lord,   50
Your leave and favour to return to France,
From whence though willingly I came to Denmark,
To show my duty in your coronation,
Yet now, I must confess, that duty done,
My thoughts and wishes bend again towards France   55
And bow them to your gracious leave and pardon.
King: Have you your father's leave? What says Polonius?
Polonius: He hath, my lord, wrung from me my slow leave
    By laboursome petition, and at last
    Upon his will I seal'd my hard consent;   60
    I do beseech you, give him leave to go.
King: Take thy fair hour, Laertes; time be thine,
    And thy best graces spend it at thy will!
    But now, my cousin Hamlet, and my son.
Hamlet: [*Aside.*] A little more than kin, and less than kind.   65

66	*clouds:* gloomy mood
67	*I am too much i' the sun:* This is a pun on the words "sun" and "son." The audience has been aware of the brooding figure of Hamlet throughout this scene. His first words, which are cryptic, ambiguous, and sarcastic, catch our attention.
68	*nighted colour:* Hamlet is dressed in black (in mourning) while everyone else is dressed in bright colours.
69	*Denmark:* King of Denmark (i.e., Claudius)
70	*vailed lids:* downcast eyes
72	*'tis common:* it's common knowledge
75	*particular:* special
76-86	In this speech, Hamlet introduces an important theme in the play: the difference between how things *appear* and how they *really are.* Much of the plot and symbolism of the play stems from this contrast.
79	*windy suspiration of forced breath:* sighs
81	*dejected haviour of the visage:* sad facial expression
85	*passeth show:* is beyond what you see
86	*trappings:* outer clothing
92	*obsequious sorrow:* the required mourning at a funeral
98-99	*what we know . . . sense:* what we know is inevitable (i.e., death) and is one of the commonest things we experience.

King: How is it that the clouds still hang on you?
Hamlet: Not so, my lord; I am too much i' the sun.
Queen: Good Hamlet, cast thy nighted colour off,
    And let thine eye look like a friend on Denmark.
    Do not for ever with thy vailed lids   70
    Seek for thy noble father in the dust:
    Thou know'st 'tis common; all that lives must die,
    Passing through nature to eternity.
Hamlet: Ay, madam, it is common.
Queen: If it be,
    Why seems it so particular with thee?   75
Hamlet: Seems, madam! nay, it is; I know not "seems."
    'Tis not alone my inky cloak, good mother,
    Nor customary suits of solemn black,
    Nor windy suspiration of forced breath,
    No, nor the fruitful river in the eye,   80
    Nor the dejected haviour of the visage,
    Together with all forms, modes, shapes of grief,
    That can denote me truly: these indeed seem,
    For they are actions that a man might play;
    But I have that within which passeth show;   85
    These, but the trappings and the suits of woe.
King: 'Tis sweet and commendable in your nature, Hamlet,
    To give these mourning duties to your father:
    But, you must know, your father lost a father,
    That father lost, lost his, and the survivor bound 90
    In filial obligation for some term
    To do obsequious sorrow: but to persever
    In obstinate condolement is a course
    Of impious stubbornness; 'tis unmanly grief:
    It shows a will most incorrect to heaven,   95
    A heart unfortified, a mind impatient,
    An understanding simple and unschool'd:
    For what we know must be and is as common
    As any the most vulgar thing to sense,
    Why should we, in our peevish opposition   100
    Take it to heart? Fie! 'tis a fault to heaven,
    A fault against the dead, a fault to nature,
    To reason most absurd, whose common theme
    Is death of fathers, and who still hath cried,

107   *unprevailing:* useless, unavailing

109   *You are . . . throne:* In Denmark at the time, a son did not necessarily succeed his father to the throne. While some attention was paid to close blood ties, the King was elected. Therefore, Hamlet had no legal right to the throne.

113   *Wittenberg:* a town in Germany. The university there was a renowned centre of learning in Shakespeare's time.

114   *retrograde:* contrary

125   *jocund:* joyful; *health:* toast; *that Denmark drinks:* that the King drinks

125-128   Claudius looks forward to a drunken celebration during which cannons will be fired to announce each toast the King drinks.

127   *rouse:* carouse; *bruit:* echo

130   *resolve:* dissolve

132   *canon:* law

134   *uses:* routines

136-137   *Things rank . . . merely:* This is the first of a chain of images in the play which suggest an unnatural invasion of some disease, which eventually poisons the whole organism.

137   *merely:* completely

140   *Hyperion:* the sun-god in Greek mythology; *satyr:* a creature part man and part goat in Greek mythology. Satyrs were lewd and promiscuous.

141   *beteem:* allow

From the first corse till he that died to-day,　　　　105
"This must be so." We pray you, throw to earth
This unprevailing woe; and think of us
As of a father: for let the world take note,
You are the most immediate to our throne,
And, with no less nobility of love　　　　110
Than that which dearest father bears his son,
Do I impart towards you. For your intent
In going back to school in Wittenberg,
It is most retrograde to our desire:
And, we beseech you, bend you to remain　　　　115
Here, in the cheer and comfort of our eye,
Our chiefest courtier, cousin and our son.
Queen: Let not thy mother lose her prayers, Hamlet:
　　I pray thee, stay with us; go not to Wittenberg.
Hamlet: I shall in all my best obey you, madam.　　　　120
King: Why, 'tis a loving and a fair reply;
　　Be as ourself in Denmark. Madam, come;
　　This gentle and unforced accord of Hamlet
　　Sits smiling to my heart: in grace whereof,
　　No jocund health that Denmark drinks to-day,　　　　125
　　But the great cannon to the clouds shall tell,
　　And the king's rouse the heavens shall bruit again,
　　Re-speaking earthly thunder. Come away.
　　　　　　　　　　　　[Exeunt all but Hamlet.]
Hamlet: O, that this too too-solid flesh would melt,
　　Thaw, and resolve itself into a dew!　　　　130
　　Or that the Everlasting had not fix'd
　　His canon 'gainst self-slaughter! God! O God!
　　How weary, stale, flat, and unprofitable
　　Seem to me all the uses of this world!
　　Fie on't! O fie! 'tis an unweeded garden,　　　　135
　　That grows to seed; things rank and gross in nature
　　Possess it merely. That it should come to this!
　　But two months dead! nay, not so much, not two;
　　So excellent a king; that was, to this,
　　Hyperion to a satyr: so loving to my mother,　　　　140
　　That he might not beteem the winds of heaven
　　Visit her face too roughly. Heaven and earth!
　　Must I remember? why, she would hang on him,

147   *ere:* before

149   *Niobe:* Niobe, Queen of Thebes, wept when her fourteen children were killed as a punishment for her boasting about them. Zeus eventually turned Niobe into stone.

150   *wants discourse of reason:* lacks the ability to reason

153   *Hercules:* a hero in Greek mythology renowned for his great strength

154-155   *Ere yet . . . eyes:* before the redness (from hypocritically crying over her husband's death) had left her inflamed eyes

156   *to post:* to run quickly

163   *I'll change . . . you:* I'll be your servant, you be my friend; or, I'll exchange the name of friend with you.

171   *truster:* believer

173   *affair:* business

178   *hard upon:* soon afterward

179-180   *Thrift . . . tables:* The wedding was held so quickly in order to save money by serving the food left over from the funeral observances.

As if increase of appetite had grown
By what it fed on: and yet, within a month—   145
Let me not think on't—Frailty, thy name is woman!—
A little month, or ere those shoes were old
With which she followed my poor father's body,
Like Niobe, all tears;—why she, even she,—
O God! a beast that wants discourse of reason   150
Would have mourn'd longer,—married with mine uncle,
My father's brother, but no more like my father
Than I to Hercules: within a month;
Ere yet the salt of most unrighteous tears
Had left the flushing of her galled eyes,   155
She married:—O most wicked speed, to post
With such dexterity to incestuous sheets!
It is not, nor it cannot come to, good;
But break, my heart, for I must hold my tongue!

[Enter Horatio, Bernardo, and Marcellus.]

Horatio: Hail to your lordship!
Hamlet: I am glad to see you well: 160
   Horatio,—or I do forget myself,
Horatio: The same, my lord, and your poor servant ever.
Hamlet: Sir, my good friend; I'll change that name with you.
   And what make you from Wittenberg, Horatio?
   Marcellus?
Marcellus: My good lord?   165
Hamlet: I am very glad to see you. Good even, sir.
   But what, in faith, make you from Wittenberg?
Horatio: A truant disposition, good my lord.
Hamlet: I would not hear your enemy say so,
   Nor shall you do mine ear that violence,   170
   To make it truster of your own report
   Against yourself: I know you are no truant.
   But what is your affair in Elsinore?
   We'll teach you to drink deep ere you depart.
Horatio: My lord, I came to see your father's funeral.   175
Hamlet: I pray thee, do not mock me, fellow-student;
   I think it was to see my mother's wedding.
Horatio: Indeed, my lord, it follow'd hard upon.
Hamlet: Thrift, thrift, Horatio! the funeral baked meats

181   *dearest:* worst

191   *Season your admiration:* restrain your astonishment
192   *attent:* attentive

199   *to point:* fully, in readiness; *cap-à-pé:* head to foot

203   *truncheon:* staff; *distill'd:* melted
204   *act:* operation

208   *deliver'd:* reported

211   *These hands . . . like:* My two hands are no more like one
another (than are the Ghost and Hamlet's father).
212   *platform:* ramparts

Did coldly furnish forth the marriage tables.   180
Would I had met my dearest foe in heaven
Ere I had seen that day, Horatio!
My father!—methinks, I see my father.
Horatio: O, where, my lord?
Hamlet: In my mind's eye, Horatio.
Horatio: I saw him once; he was a goodly king.   185
Hamlet: He was a man, take him for all in all,
    I shall not look upon his like again.
Horatio: My lord, I think I saw him yesternight.
Hamlet: Saw! who?
Horatio: My lord, the king your father.
Hamlet: The king my father!   190
Horatio: Season your admiration for a while
    With an attent ear, till I may deliver,
    Upon the witness of these gentlemen,
    This marvel to you.
Hamlet: For God's love, let me hear.
Horatio: Two nights together had these gentlemen,   195
    Marcellus and Bernardo, on their watch,
    In the dead waste and middle of the night,
    Been thus encounter'd. A figure like your father,
    Armed to point, exactly, cap-à-pé,
    Appears before them, and with solemn march   200
    Goes slow and stately by them: thrice he walk'd,
    By their oppress'd and fear-surprised eyes,
    Within his truncheon's length; whilst they, distill'd
    Almost to jelly with the act of fear,
    Stand dumb, and speak not to him. This to me   205
    In dreadful secrecy impart they did;
    And I with them the third night kept the watch:
    Where, as they had deliver'd, both in time,
    Form of the thing, each word made true and good,
    The apparition comes: I knew your father: 210
    These hands are not more like.
Hamlet: But where was this?
Marcellus: My lord, upon the platform where we watch'd.
Hamlet: Did you not speak to it?
Horatio: My lord, I did,
    But answer made it none: yet once methought

228   *beaver:* the part of the helmet that can be lifted up (visor)

230   *countenance:* expression

236   *tell:* count

238   *grizzled:* partly grey

240   *sable silver'd:* black streaked with silver

It lifted up its head and did address   215
Itself to motion, like as it would speak:
But even then the morning cock crew loud,
And at the sound it shrunk in haste away
And vanish'd from our sight.
Hamlet: 'Tis very strange.
Horatio: As I do live, my honour'd lord, 'tis true;   220
And we did think it writ down in our duty
To let you know of it.
Hamlet: Indeed, indeed, sirs, but this troubles me.
Hold you the watch to-night?
All: We do, my lord.
Hamlet: Arm'd, say you?
All: Arm'd, my lord.   225
Hamlet: From top to toe?
All: My lord, from head to foot.
Hamlet: Then saw you not his face?
Horatio: O yes, my lord; he wore his beaver up.
Hamlet: What, look'd he frowningly?
Horatio: A countenance more in sorrow than in anger.   230
Hamlet: Pale, or red?
Horatio: Nay, very pale.
Hamlet: And fix'd his eyes upon you?
Horatio: Most constantly.
Hamlet: I would I had been there.
Horatio: It would have much amazed you.
Hamlet: Very like, very like. Stay'd it long?   235
Horatio: While one with moderate haste might tell a hundred.
Marcellus, Bernardo: Longer, longer.
Horatio: Not when I saw't.
Hamlet: His beard was grizzled? no?
Horatio: It was as I have seen it in his life,
A sable silver'd.
Hamlet: I will watch to-night;   240
Perhance 'twill walk again.
Horatio: I warrant it will.
Hamlet: If it assume my noble father's person,
I'll speak to it, though hell itself should gape
And bid me hold my peace. I pray you all,
If you have hitherto conceal'd this sight,   245

246   *Let it be . . . still:* Remain silent on this subject.

249   *requite your loves:* reward you for your efforts

252   *Your love . . . you:* I would rather have your love, as you have mine.

254   *doubt:* suspect

Let it be tenable in your silence still,
And whatsoever else shall hap to-night,
Give it an understanding, but no tongue;
I will requite your loves. So fare you well:
Upon the platform, 'twixt eleven and twelve,   250
I'll visit you.
All: Our duty to your honour.
Hamlet: Your love, as mine to you: farewell.
                    [*Exeunt Horatio, Marcellus, and Bernardo.*]
My father's spirit in arms! all is not well;
I doubt some foul play: would the night were come!
Till then sit still, my soul. Foul deeds will rise,   255
Though all the earth o'erwhelm them, to men's eyes.
                                        [*Exit.*]

Act 1, Scene 2: Activities

1. Choose one of the following activities. Brainstorm and organize your ideas before beginning to write.

   a) In the role of a television news journalist, prepare a commentary about the court session. Give some background to Claudius' speech and provide your own observations. Before you begin writing, decide whether your television network supports Claudius' accession to the throne. Have your classmates comment on the bias that you reveal in your commentary. Identify how that bias was created.

   b) In the role of Claudius, write two entries in your private diary, one before and one after holding court. Include your innermost thoughts, your hopes and fears, and your assessment of how the court session went. Your classmates will comment on whether the diary entries correspond to their impressions of Claudius to this point.

   c) In the role of Queen Gertrude's lady-in-waiting, write a letter to a close friend. Include the inside gossip of the palace, your reaction to Gertrude's hasty remarriage, and your impression of Gertrude's appearance and behaviour during the court scene. You may use background information. The drawing at the beginning of this scene may give you some hints, as would the viewing of this scene on video or DVD.

   d) In the role of court observer, write a report on Hamlet's character. You have been present at the court session, and observed his body language in talking with his friends at the end of the scene. Give your assessment of Hamlet's state of mind and its causes. (Remember that as a court observer you would not have seen or heard Hamlet's soliloquy.) Your classmates will comment on how objective your report is and on how well you support your opinions with examples of specific behaviour. The format for the report could be: personal history, reason for concern, observations, opinions, predictions.

2. With your group, explore the image of a garden, as Hamlet uses it in lines 135–6. Your ideas will be useful when you encounter garden imagery later in the play. Draw a chart with three columns. The headings are "a well-kept garden," "an unweeded garden," and "comments." Under the first two headings, write details that you think would describe each kind of garden. If you are not satisfied with your information, ask someone who spends a lot of time gardening. In the third column, make a comment that draws a parallel between this kind of garden and the government of a country.

3. With a partner, look at Hamlet's first soliloquy, lines 129–159, concentrating on the punctuation only. What impression do you have of Hamlet's state of mind from the punctuation? Share your ideas with the class.

4. "But break, my heart, for I must hold my tongue!" (Line 159) In your journal, reflect on a situation where, like Hamlet, you had to keep silent about something that bothered you. Would it have been better to communicate about it? To whom?

For the next scene . . .

In your journal, write about a time when an older person gave you advice which you knew that person would not follow himself or herself. What were the results? How did you feel afterward?

Act 1, Scene 3

In this scene . . .

This scene familiarizes us with Polonius' family. Laertes
is about to leave for France and is saying goodbye to
his sister, Ophelia. He takes the opportunity to warn her
about her romance with Hamlet. Polonius arrives and
gives Laertes advice about how to behave in France.
Once Laertes has departed, Polonius also warns
Ophelia that Hamlet's intentions may not be honourable,
and he tells her to avoid him. After attempting to defend
her relationship with Hamlet to Polonius, Ophelia
accepts her father's advice.

2-4	Laertes is asking his sister to write to him every day there is means to send a letter.
2	*give benefit:* are favourable
3	*convoy is assistant:* a ship is available
6	*fashion:* passing fancy, something changeable and temporary; *toy in blood:* impulsive behaviour
7	*youth of primy nature:* early spring
8	*forward:* ripening too early (and therefore likely to rot quickly)
9	*the perfume . . . minute:* brief pleasure (one that lasts only a moment)
11	*crescent:* growing
12	*thews and bulks:* muscle power and body size; *as this temple waxes:* as we grow
14	*withal:* at the same time
15-16	*now no . . . will:* Now no stain or deceit mars his good intentions.
15	*cautel:* deceit
17	*His greatness weigh'd:* when you consider his high position
19	*unvalued:* unimportant
20	*Carve for himself:* make his own (selfish) decisions
23	*yielding:* approval
25-27	*It fits . . . deed:* You would be wise to believe it only to the extent that his situation will allow him to keep his word.

Scene 3

A room in Polonius' house.
Enter Laertes and Ophelia.

Laertes: My necessities are embark'd; farewell;
   And, sister, as the winds give benefit,
   And convoy is assistant, do not sleep,
   But let me hear from you.
Ophelia: Do you doubt that?
Laertes: For Hamlet, and the trifling of his favour,   5
   Hold it a fashion, and a toy in blood,
   A violet in the youth of primy nature,
   Forward, not permanent, sweet, not lasting,
   The perfume and suppliance of a minute;
   No more.
Ophelia: No more but so?
Laertes: Think it no more: 10
   For nature crescent does not grow alone
   In thews and bulk; but, as this temple waxes,
   The inward service of the mind and soul
   Grows wide withal. Perhaps he loves you now;
   And now no soil nor cautel doth besmirch   15
   The virtue of his will; but you must fear,
   His greatness weigh'd, his will is not his own;
   For he himself is subject to his birth:
   He may not, as unvalued persons do,
   Carve for himself, for on his choice depends   20
   The safety and the health of the whole state;
   And therefore must his choice be circumscribed
   Under the voice and yielding of that body
   Whereof he is the head. Then if he says he loves you,
   It fits your wisdom so far to believe it   25
   As he in his peculiar act and place
   May give his saying deed; which is no further
   Than the main voice of Denmark goes withal.

30	*credent:* believing; *list:* listen to
31	*chaste treasure:* virginity
32	*unmaster'd importunity:* uncontrolled insistence
34	*keep within . . . affection:* Do not let emotions overpower judgment.
36-37	*The chariest maid . . . moon:* Even the most prudent girl can become reckless.
38	*Virtue itself . . . strokes:* Even virtuous people cannot escape evil gossip.
39-40	*The canker . . . disclosed:* The canker worm too often destroys early spring flowers even before they blossom.
41-42	*And in the morn . . . imminent:* And just as destructive blights occur in the morning, so violent emotions most often occur in young people.
44	*Youth . . . near:* Young people rebel against restrictions even when no one else tempts them.
47	*ungracious:* wicked
49	*puff'd:* bloated; *libertine:* loose, self-indulgent person
50	*primrose path of dalliance:* the enjoyable, easy path of pleasure
51	*recks not his own rede:* doesn't take his own advice; *fear me not:* Don't worry about me.
59	*character:* engrave (the thoughts)
60	*Nor any . . . act:* If you have an unsuitable thought, don't put it into action.
61	*Be thou . . . vulgar:* Don't socialize too much with ordinary people. (Be friendly, but don't give away too much of yourself.)
62	*their adoption tried:* their friendship tested
63	*Grapple . . . steel:* bind them to you tightly (like the metal hoops that hold a barrel together)
64-65	*But do not . . . comrade:* Do not cheapen friendship by welcoming every unproven associate.

Then weigh what loss your honour may sustain,
If with too credent ear you list his songs,   30
Or lose your heart, or your chaste treasure open
To his unmaster'd importunity.
Fear it, Ophelia, fear it, my dear sister,
And keep within the rear of your affection,
Out of the shot and danger of desire.   35
The chariest maid is prodigal enough,
If she unmask her beauty to the moon:
Virtue itself 'scapes not calumnious strokes:
The canker galls the infants of the spring
Too oft before their buttons be disclosed,   40
And in the morn and liquid dew of youth
Contagious blastments are most imminent.
Be wary then; best safety lies in fear;
Youth to itself rebels, though none else near.
Ophelia: I shall the effect of this good lesson keep,   45
As watchman to my heart. But, good my brother,
Do not, as some ungracious pastors do,
Show me the steep and thorny way to heaven,
Whilst, like a puff'd and reckless libertine,
Himself the primrose path of dalliance treads   50
And recks not his own rede.
Laertes: O fear me not.
I stay too long; but here my father comes.

[Enter Polonius.]

O double blessing is a double grace;
Occasion smiles upon a second leave.
Polonius: Yet here, Laertes! aboard, aboard, for shame!   55
The wind sits in the shoulder of your sail,
And you are stay'd for. There; my blessing with thee!
                    [Laying his hand on Laertes' head.]
And these few precepts in thy memory
See thou character. Give thy thoughts no tongue,
Nor any unproportion'd thought his act.   60
Be thou familiar, but by no means vulgar.
The friends thou hast, and their adoption tried,
Grapple them to thy soul with hoops of steel,
But do not dull thy palm with entertainment

65   *new-hatch'd, unfledged:* immature

69   *censure:* opinion
70   *habit:* clothing

77   *husbandry:* thrift

81   *my blessing . . . thee:* My blessing is that this advice will bear fruit in you.
83   *tend:* wait

90   *Marry:* a mild oath; originally, "By the Virgin Mary"

94   *put on me:* told to me

97   *behoves:* suits
99   *tenders:* offers
102   *Unsifted:* lacking experience
103-109 Polonius is punning on the word "tenders." He uses it to mean "offers of love" (1.103), "credit notes" as opposed to real money (1.106), "value" (1.107) and "render" or "change into" (1.109).

Of each new-hatch'd, unfledged comrade. Beware   65
Of entrance to a quarrel; but, being in,
Bear't that the opposed may beware of thee.
Give every man thine ear, but few thy voice:
Take each man's censure, but reserve thy judgment.
Costly thy habit as thy purse can buy,   70
But not express'd in fancy; rich, not gaudy:
For the apparel oft proclaims the man;
And they in France of the best rank and station
Are most select and generous chief in that.
Neither a borrower nor a lender be: 75
For loan oft loses both itself and friend,
And borrowing dulls the edge of husbandry.
This above all: to thine own self be true,
And it must follow, as the night the day,
Thou canst not then be false to any man.   80
Farewell: my blessing season this in thee!
Laertes: Most humbly do I take my leave, my lord.
Polonius: The time invites you; go, your servants tend.
Laertes: Farewell, Ophelia; and remember well
    What I have said to you.
Ophelia: 'Tis in my memory lock'd,   85
    And you yourself shall keep the key of it.
Laertes: Farewell.   *[Exit Laertes.]*
Polonius: What is't, Ophelia, he hath said to you?
Ophelia: So please you, something touching the lord Hamlet.
Polonius: Marry, well bethought: 90
    'Tis told me, he hath very oft of late
    Given private time to you, and you yourself
    Have of your audience been most free and bounteous:
    If it be so—as so 'tis put on me,
    And that in way of caution—I must tell you,   95
    You do not understand yourself so clearly
    As it behoves my daughter and your honour.
    What is between you? give me up the truth.
Ophelia: He hath, my lord, of late, made many tenders
    Of his affection to me.   100
Polonius: Affection? pooh! you speak like a green girl,
    Unsifted in such perilous circumstance,
    Do you believe his tenders, as you call them?

108	*not to crack . . . phrase:* not to overwork the pun like a horse that's been ridden too hard
112	*go to, go to:* nonsense, don't be silly
113	*countenance:* an expression of sincerity
115	*springes to catch woodcocks:* Woodcocks were considered to be stupid birds that could be caught easily in snares.
116	*prodigal:* freely, generously
117-120	*these blazes . . . fire:* Polonius is pointing out the difference between shallow emotions, which die quickly (small blazes), and true love (fire).
121	*Be somewhat . . . presence:* Appear in public less often.
122-123	*Set . . . parley:* Make yourself more valuable by not responding to his every request.
125	*tether:* freedom, range
127-131	*Do not believe . . . beguile:* Do not believe in his promises, for they are not what they seem. They appear to be innocent, but their purpose is to trick you.
127	*brokers:* agents, go-betweens
128	*dye:* colour; also, quality; *investments:* priestly garments
130	*bonds:* marriage bonds
133	*slander:* misuse

Ophelia: I do not know, my lord, what I should think.
Polonius: Marry, I'll teach you: think yourself a baby, 105
    That you have ta'en these tenders for true pay,
    Which are not sterling. Tender yourself more dearly;
    Or—not to crack the wind of the poor phrase,
    Running it thus—you'll tender me a fool.
Ophelia: My lord, he hath importuned me with love 110
    In honourable fashion.
Polonius: Ay, fashion you may call it; go to, go to.
Ophelia: And hath given countenance to his speech, my
       lord,
    With almost all the holy vows of heaven.
Polonius: Ay, springes to catch woodcocks. I do know, 115
    When the blood burns, how prodigal the soul
    Gives the tongue vows: these blazes, daughter,
    Giving more light than heat, extinct in both,
    Even in their promise, as it is a making,
    You must not take for fire. From this time, daughter, 120
    Be somewhat scanter of your maiden presence;
    Set your entreatments at a higher rate
    Than a command to parley. For lord Hamlet,
    Believe so much in him, that he is young,
    And with a larger tether may he walk, 125
    Than may be given you: in few, Ophelia,
    Do not believe his vows; for they are brokers,
    Not of that dye which their investments show,
    But mere implorators of unholy suits,
    Breathing like sanctified and pious bonds, 130
    The better to beguile. This is for all:
    I would not, in plain terms, from this time forth,
    Have you so slander any moment's leisure,
    As to give words or talk with the lord Hamlet.
    Look to't, I charge you: come your ways. 135
Ophelia: I shall obey, my lord.   [*Exeunt.*]

Act 1, Scene 3: Activities

1. With a partner, make point-form notes on Laertes' advice to Ophelia and Ophelia's response (lines 5–44). Then role-play this conversation between brother and sister in informal contemporary language. Discuss with your partner whether the advice would be valid today.

2. What advice might an older brother give a younger sister nowadays about her first romance? What advice might an older sister give a younger brother about his first love? How does Ophelia respond to Laertes' advice? What does this suggest to you about their relationship? Discuss your ideas in your group.

3. What advice might a modern parent give a near-adult child who is leaving home to live in another city? Divide the class into five groups. Each group will discuss one of these topics: choosing friends, solving conflicts with others, clothes, money, basic values. After hearing the class's advice, review Polonius' advice to Laertes (lines 58–81) and discuss similarities and differences.

4. Suppose that you are studying families in history. Make notes on the relationships in the Polonius family. Consider the relative position of men and women in the family, parent–child roles, and power. Share your observations with the class.

5. Write a diary entry in the role of Ophelia. As Ophelia, you could write about your responses to your brother's departure, your feelings about palace gossip, and your reaction to your father's description of Hamlet's behaviour. Do you agree that you should stop seeing Hamlet? Comment on how much control you have over your own life.

6. Look at the illustrations for Scene 1, Scene 2, and Scene 3. What feeling do you get about the architecture of the palace? What would it feel like to be there? What sorts of things would you see, hear, and smell?

For the next scene . . .

Have you ever refused to join in a group's activity because you didn't like the behaviour of the people in that group? Did you tell them how you felt? Did your refusal to join the activity make you feel like an outsider? Write a journal entry about this experience.

Act 1, Scene 4

In this scene . . .

Twenty-four hours have passed since the Ghost appeared in Scene 1. Hamlet, Horatio, and Marcellus are on the platform of the castle waiting for the Ghost to reappear. In the background, the blaring of trumpets and the sound of cannons being fired announce each drink the King takes as he carouses through the night. When the Ghost appears, Hamlet questions it. The Ghost beckons Hamlet to follow. Despite his friends' warnings, Hamlet ignores the possible dangers and follows his father's Ghost.

1 *shrewdly:* sharply

2 *eager:* keen, sharp

6 *held his wont to walk:* was accustomed to walk

8 *The king doth wake to-night:* The King is having a celebration tonight; *rouse:* a large glass (Claudius is drinking heavily.)

9 *keeps wassail:* is drinking toasts to his guests; *up-spring:* a wild dance, originating in Germany

10 *Rhenish:* Rhine wine

15 *to the manner born:* accustomed to it from birth

16 *More honour'd . . . observance:* a custom that is better *not* practised

18 *traduced:* slandered; *tax'd:* criticized

19 *clepe:* call; *with swinish phrase:* The Danes are being called pigs.

20 *addition:* good name

22 *attribute:* reputation

24 *vicious mole of nature:* a harmful natural blemish

27 *o'ergrowth of some complexion:* In Shakespeare's time, it was believed that human nature was governed by four fluids (called "humours"): blood, black bile, yellow bile and phlegm. Too much of any one fluid would change a person's temperament (complexion), making him or her sanguine, melancholic, choleric or phlegmatic.

Scene 4

The platform.
Enter Hamlet, Horatio, and
Marcellus.

Hamlet: The air bites shrewdly: it is very cold.
Horatio: It is a nipping and an eager air.
Hamlet: What hour now?
Horatio: I think it lacks of twelve.
Marcellus: No, it is struck.
Horatio: Indeed? I heard it not; then it draws near the season   5
 Wherein the spirit held his wont to walk.
   [*A flourish of trumpets, and ordnance shot off, within.*]
 What does this mean, my lord?
Hamlet: The king doth wake to-night, and takes his rouse,
 Keeps wassail, and the swaggering up-spring reels;
 And as he drains his draughts of Rhenish down,   10
 The kettle-drum and trumpet thus bray out
 The triumph of his pledge.
Horatio: Is it a custom?
Hamlet: Ay, marry, is't:
 And to my mind, though I am native here
 And to the manner born, it is a custom   15
 More honour'd in the breach than the observance.
 This heavy-headed revel east and west
 Makes us traduced and tax'd of other nations:
 They clepe us drunkards, and with swinish phrase
 Soil our addition; and, indeed, it takes   20
 From our achievements, though perform'd at height,
 The pith and marrow of our attribute.
 So, oft it chances in particular men,
 That for some vicious mole of nature in them,
 As, in their birth,—wherein they are not guilty.   25
 Since nature cannot choose his origin—
 By the o'ergrowth of some complexion,

28   *pales and forts:* defences

29   *o'er-leavens:* spoils

30   *plausive:* pleasing

31   *the stamp of one defect:* This refers to the "mole" in line 24.

32   *livery:* badge

36-38   *The dram of evil . . . scandal:* A small defect will ruin the whole personality. (This notion relates to the chain of poison/garden images that appear throughout the play.)

43   *questionable shape:* as if you want me to question you

47   *canonized:* buried according to Church ceremonies; *hearsed:* put in a coffin

48   *cerements:* shrouds

52   *complete steel:* full armour

54   *fools of nature:* mortals who do not understand the mysteries of life

55   *to shake our disposition:* to upset us, to disturb our minds

59   *As if . . . desire:* as if it wanted to talk to you; *impartment:* message

Oft breaking down the pales and forts of reason,
Or by some habit that too much o'er-leavens
The form of plausive manners, that these men—   30
Carrying, I say, the stamp of one defect,
Being nature's livery, or fortune's star,
Their virtues else—be they as pure as grace,
As infinite as man may undergo—
Shall in the general censure take corruption   35
From that particular fault: the dram of evil
Doth all the noble substance of a doubt
To his own scandal—

[Enter Ghost.]

Horatio: Look, my lord, it comes!
Hamlet: Angels and ministers of grace defend us!
  Be thou a spirit of health or goblin damn'd,   40
  Bring with thee airs from heaven or blasts from hell,
  Be thy intents wicked or charitable,
  Thou com'st in such a questionable shape
  That I will speak to thee: I'll call thee Hamlet,
  King, father, royal Dane: O, answer me!   45
  Let me not burst in ignorance, but tell
  Why thy canonized bones, hearsed in death,
  Have burst their cerements; why the sepulchre,
  Wherein we saw thee quietly in-urn'd,
  Hath oped his ponderous and marble jaws,   50
  To cast thee up again. What may this mean,
  That thou, dead corse, again, in complete steel,
  Revisit'st thus the glimpses of the moon,
  Making night hideous; and we fools of nature
  So horridly to shake our disposition   55
  With thoughts beyond the reaches of our souls?
  Say, why is this? wherefore? what should we do?
                          [Ghost beckons Hamlet.]
Horatio: It beckons you to go away with it,
  As if it some impartment did desire
  To you alone.   60
Marcellus: Look, with what courteous action
  It waves you to a more removed ground;
  But do not go with it.

65   *at a pin's fee:* worth a pin

71   *beetles o'er:* overhangs

73   *Which might . . . reason:* which might rob you of your ability to reason

75   *toys of desperation:* desperate thoughts

83   *Nemean lion:* In Greek mythology, one of the twelve labours of Hercules was to fetch the Nemean lion's skin.

85   *lets:* hinders

Horatio: No, by no means.
Hamlet: It will not speak; then will I follow it.
Horatio: Do not, my lord.
Hamlet: Why, what should be the fear?
   I do not set my life at a pin's fee; 65
   And for my soul, what can it do to that,
   Being a thing immortal as itself?
   It waves me forth again: I'll follow it.
Horatio: What if it tempt you toward the flood, my lord,
   Or to the dreadful summit of the cliff 70
   That beetles o'er his base into the sea,
   And there assume some other horrible form,
   Which might deprive your sovereignty of reason
   And draw you into madness? think of it:
   The very place puts toys of desperation, 75
   Without more motive, into every brain
   That looks so many fathoms to the sea
   And hears it roar beneath.
Hamlet: It waves me still.
   Go on; I'll follow thee.
Marcellus: You shall not go, my lord.
Hamlet: Hold off your hands. 80
Horatio: Be ruled; you shall not go.
Hamlet: My fate cries out,
   And makes each petty artery in this body
   As hardy as the Nemean lion's nerve.—
   Still am I call'd; unhand me, gentlemen;
   By heaven, I'll make a ghost of him that lets me; 85
   I say, away! Go on; I'll follow thee.
                            [Exeunt Ghost and Hamlet.]
Horatio: He waxes desperate with imagination.
Marcellus: Let's follow; 'tis not fit thus to obey him.
Horatio: Have after. To what issue will this come?
Marcellus: Something is rotten in the state of Denmark. 90
Horatio: Heaven will direct it.
Marcellus: Nay, let's follow him.
                                      [Exeunt.]

Act 1, Scene 4: Activities

1. Recall an occasion you experienced with family members or friends when someone's behaviour made you uncomfortable or embarrassed. In your journal, describe how you dealt with the situation at the time. How did this experience affect your feelings about that person? Can you relate these feelings to Hamlet's feelings at the beginning of the scene? Explain your answer.

2. In groups, discuss what you think Hamlet is saying about human nature (lines 23–38). Structure your discussion as follows:

   • Summarize Hamlet's ideas.

   • Think of one or more individuals, past or present, whose lives illustrate Hamlet's theory. In each case, describe the person's character flaw and explain how it affected the course of his or her life.

   • Discuss whether or not an individual is responsible for his or her weaknesses.

3. In pairs, take the roles of Marcellus and Horatio and write a dialogue that takes place after Hamlet has gone to follow the Ghost. How do you feel about Hamlet's behaviour in this scene? Read your dialogue to other pairs or to the class.

For the next scene . . .

In your journal, reflect on a moment when you received some unexpected news and thought, "This news will change my life." As you think back, to what extent *did* it change your life?

Act 1, Scene 5
In this scene . . .

The Ghost tells Hamlet that he was murdered by Claudius. He accuses Claudius and Gertrude of having an adulterous relationship before his death, and he describes exactly how he was poisoned. The Ghost commands Hamlet to take revenge for these wrongs. Hamlet is horrified by all he learns and swears to follow the Ghost's commands. When he is joined by Horatio and Marcellus, he does not reveal what the Ghost told him. As his friends try to calm him, he forces them to swear secrecy about what they have seen.

2   *Mark me:* Listen.

3   *sulphurous and tormenting flames:* a description of purgatory

13   *burnt and purged away:* Hamlet's father died without receiving the last rites of the Church. As a result, his soul is caught in purgatory, since any sins he committed in his lifetime were not absolved.

21   *eternal blazon:* telling of the secrets of eternity

Scene 5

A more remote part of the platform.
Enter Ghost and Hamlet.

Hamlet: Whither wilt thou lead me? speak; I'll go no further.
Ghost: Mark me.
Hamlet: I will.
Ghost: My hour is almost come,
  When I to sulphurous and tormenting flames
  Must render up myself.
Hamlet: Alas, poor ghost!
Ghost: Pity me not, but lend thy serious hearing   5
  To what I shall unfold.
Hamlet: Speak, I am bound to hear.
Ghost: So art thou to revenge, when thou shalt hear.
Hamlet: What!
Ghost: I am thy father's spirit;
  Doom'd for a certain term to walk the night,   10
  And for the day confined to fast in fires,
  Till the foul crimes done in my days of nature
  Are burnt and purged away. But that I am forbid
  To tell the secrets of my prison-house,
  I could a tale unfold whose lightest word   15
  Would harrow up thy soul; freeze thy young blood,
  Make thy two eyes, like stars, start from their spheres,
  Thy knotted and combined locks to part
  And each particular hair to stand on end,
  Like quills upon the fretful porcupine;   20
  But this eternal blazon must not be
  To ears of flesh and blood. List, list, O, list!
  If thou didst ever thy dear father love,—
Hamlet: O God!
Ghost: Revenge his foul and most unnatural murder.   25
Hamlet: Murder?

27   *in the best:* at best

33   *Lethe:* In Greek mythology, Lethe is the river of forgetfulness located in the underworld.

35   *orchard:* garden

37   *forged process:* false story

38   *abused:* misled

51   *decline:* fall to a lower level

62   *Upon my secure hour:* at a time when I was unsuspecting

63   *hebenon:* a poison plant

65   *leperous distilment:* juices as deadly as leprosy

Ghost: Murder most foul, as in the best it is,
   But this most foul, strange, and unnatural.
Hamlet: Haste me to know't; that I, with wings as swift
   As meditation or the thoughts of love,   30
   May sweep to my revenge.
Ghost: I find thee apt;
   And duller shouldst thou be than the fat weed
   That rots itself in ease on Lethe wharf,
   Wouldst thou not stir in this. Now, Hamlet, hear:
   'Tis given out that, sleeping in mine orchard,   35
   A serpent stung me; so the whole ear of Denmark
   Is by a forged process of my death
   Rankly abused: but know, thou noble youth,
   The serpent that did sting thy father's life
   Now wears his crown.   40
Hamlet: My uncle?
   O my prophetic soul!
Ghost: Ay, that incestuous, that adulterate beast,
   With witchcraft of his wit, with traitorous gifts,—
   O wicked wit and gifts, that have the power   45
   So to seduce!—won to his shameful lust
   The will of my most seeming-virtuous queen;
   O Hamlet, what a falling-off was there!
   From me, whose love was of that dignity
   That it went hand in hand even with the vow   50
   I made to her in marriage; and to decline
   Upon a wretch, whose natural gifts were poor
   To those of mine!
   But virtue, as it never will be moved,
   Though lewdness court it in a shape of heaven,   55
   So lust, though to a radiant angel link'd,
   Will sate itself in a celestial bed,
   And prey on garbage.
   But soft! methinks, I scent the morning air;
   Brief let me be. Sleeping within mine orchard,   60
   My custom always in the afternoon,
   Upon my secure hour thy uncle stole,
   With juice of cursed hebenon in a vial,
   And in the porches of mine ears did pour
   The leperous distilment; whose effect   65

69-70	*it doth posset/And curd:* it curdles and clots (the blood)
70	*eager:* acidic. The reference is to rennet, which is added to milk to curdle it.
72	*a most instant tetter bark'd about:* My skin became as rough and scaly as tree bark.
73	*lazar-like:* like leprosy
76	*despatch'd:* deprived
78	*unhousel'd, disappointed, unaneled:* without the proper religious ceremonies
82	*nature:* that which is natural to humans
84	*luxury:* lechery
90	*matin:* morning
98	*globe:* head
99	*table:* notebook (related to the word "tablet")
100	*fond:* foolish
101	*saws:* sayings; *pressures:* impressions

Holds such an enmity with blood of man
That swift as quicksilver it courses through
The natural gates and alleys of the body;
And, with a sudden vigour, it doth posset
And curd, like eager droppings into milk,   70
The thin and wholesome blood: so did it mine;
And a most instant tetter bark'd about
Most lazar-like, with vile and loathsome crust,
All my smooth body.
Thus was I, sleeping, by a brother's hand   75
Of life, of crown, of queen, at once despatch'd;
Cut off even in the blossoms of my sin,
Unhousel'd, disappointed, unaneled;
No reckoning made, but sent to my account
With all my imperfections on my head.   80
Hamlet: O, horrible! O, horrible! most horrible!
Ghost: If thou hast nature in thee, bear it not;
Let not the royal bed of Denmark be
A couch for luxury and damned incest.
But, howsoever thou pursuest this act,   85
Taint not thy mind, nor let thy soul contrive
Against thy mother aught; leave her to heaven,
And to those thorns that in her bosom lodge,
To prick and sting her. Fare thee well at once!
The glow-worm shows the matin to be near,   90
And 'gins to pale his uneffectual fire:
Adieu, adieu, adieu! remember me!   [*Exit.*]
Hamlet: O all you host of heaven! O earth! What else?
And shall I couple hell? O fie! Hold, hold, my heart;
And you, my sinews, grow not instant old,   95
But bear me stiffly up! Remember thee!
Ay, thou poor ghost, while memory holds a seat
In this distracted globe. Remember thee!
Yea, from the table of my memory
I'll wipe away all trivial fond records,   100
All saws of books, all forms, all pressures past,
That youth and observation copied there;
And thy commandment all alone shall live
Within the book and volume of my brain,
Unmix'd with baser matter: yes, by heaven!   105

116-17   *Illo, ho, ho . . . boy!:* a falconer's cry to his bird (a signal to us that Hamlet may not be in control of his mind).

125   *an arrant knave:* complete, utter fool

128   *without . . . at all:* without more ado

O most pernicious woman!
O villain, villain, smiling, damned villain!
My tables—meet it is I set it down,
That one may smile, and smile, and be a villain;
At least I'm sure it may be so in Denmark;   110

                                        [*Writing.*]

So, uncle, there you are. Now to my word;
It is, "Adieu, adieu! remember me."
I have sworn't.
Horatio [*Without*]: My lord, my lord,—
Marcellus [*Without*]:   Lord Hamlet,—
Horatio [*Without*]:   Heaven secure him!
Marcellus [*Without*]: So be it!   115
Horatio [*Without*]: Illo, ho, ho, my lord!
Hamlet: Hillo, ho, ho, boy! come, bird, come.

   [*Enter Horatio and Marcellus.*]

Marcellus: How is't, my noble lord?
Horatio: What news, my lord?
Hamlet: O, wonderful!
Horatio: Good my lord, tell it.
Hamlet: No, you will reveal it.   120
Horatio: Not I, my lord, by heaven.
Marcellus: Nor I, my lord.
Hamlet: How say you then; would heart of man once think
      it?
   But you'll be secret?
Horatio, Marcellus: Ay, by heaven, my lord.
Hamlet: There's ne'er a villain dwelling in all Denmark
   But he's an arrant knave.   125
Horatio: There needs no ghost, my lord, come from the
      grave
   To tell us this.
Hamlet: Why, right; you are i' the right:
   And so, without more circumstance at all,
   I hold it fit that we shake hands and part;
   You, as your business and desire shall point you;   130
   For every man has business and desire,
   Such as it is; and for mine own poor part,
   Look you, I'll go pray.

137   *St. Patrick:* the keeper of purgatory

149   *upon my sword:* The handle of the sword makes the form of
        the cross.

151   *truepenny:* honest old fellow

157   *Hic et ubique?:* (Latin) Here and everywhere?

164   *pioneer:* a soldier who dug tunnels

Horatio: These are but wild and whirling words, my lord.

Hamlet: I'm sorry they offend you, heartily;   135
    Yes, faith, heartily.

Horatio: There's no offence, my lord.

Hamlet: Yes, by St. Patrick, but there is, Horatio.
    And much offence too. Touching this vision here,
    It is an honest ghost, that let me tell you;
    For your desire to know what is between us,   140
    O'ermaster't as you may. And now, good friends,
    As you are friends, scholars, and soldiers,
    Give me one poor request.

Horatio: What is't, my lord? We will.

Hamlet: Never make known what you have seen tonight.   145

Horatio, Marcellus: My lord, we will not.

Hamlet: Nay, but swear't.

Horatio: In faith,
    My lord, not I.

Marcellus: Nor I, my lord, in faith.

Hamlet: Upon my sword.

Marcellus: We have sworn, my lord, already.

Hamlet: In deed, upon my sword, in deed.

Ghost [*Beneath*]: Swear!   150

Hamlet: Ah, ha, boy! say'st thou so? art thou there,
    truepenny?
  Come on: you hear this fellow in the cellarage:
  Consent to swear.

Horatio: Propose the oath, my lord,

Hamlet: Never to speak of this that you have seen,
    Swear by my sword.   155

Ghost [*Beneath*]: Swear!

Hamlet: Hic et ubique? then we'll shift our ground.
    Come hither, gentlemen,
    And lay your hands again upon my sword:
    Never to speak of this that you have heard,   160
    Swear by my sword.

Ghost [*Beneath*]: Swear!

Hamlet: Well said, old mole! canst work i' the ground so
    fast?
  A worthy pioneer! Once more remove, good friends.

Horatio: O day and night, but this is wondrous strange!   165

172   *meet:* suitable
173   *antic disposition:* strange (insane) behaviour

179   *ambiguous giving out:* vague suggestion or comment

Hamlet: And therefore as a stranger give it welcome.
    There are more things in heaven and earth, Horatio,
    Than are dreamt of in our philosophy.
    But come;
    Here, as before, never, so help you mercy,   170
    How strange or odd soe'er I bear myself,
    As I perchance hereafter shall think meet
    To put an antic disposition on,
    That you, at such times seeing me, never shall,
    With arms encumber'd thus, or this head-shake,   175
    Or by pronouncing of some doubtful phrase,
    As, "Well, well, we know"; or, "We could, an if we
       would";
    Or, "If we list to speak"; or, "There be, an if they
       might";—
    Or such ambiguous giving out, to note
    That you know aught of me: this not to do,   180
    So grace and mercy at your most need help you,
    Swear!
Ghost [*Beneath*]: Swear!   [*They swear.*]
Hamlet: Rest, rest, perturbed spirit! So, gentlemen,
    With all my love I do commend me to you: 185
    And what so poor a man as Hamlet is
    May do, to express his love and friending to you,
    God willing, shall not lack. Let us go in together;
    And still your fingers on your lips, I pray.
    The time is out of joint; O cursed spite,   190
    That ever I was born to set it right!—
    Nay, come, let's go together.   [*Exeunt.*]

Act 1, Scene 5: Activities

1. "O, horrible! O, horrible! most horrible!" (line 81). Select key words or phrases from the Ghost's description of how he was murdered (lines 35–80) that you think would affect Hamlet most deeply. From these words, create your own poem that intensifies the horror. Read the poem aloud to the class.

2. What instructions does the Ghost give Hamlet about Gertrude? In your journal, suggest reasons why the Ghost is concerned about Hamlet's reaction to Gertrude. If you were the Ghost, what more specific suggestions would you make to Hamlet about the way he should treat his mother?

3. Nowadays a person in Hamlet's situation might use the legal system to obtain justice. However, even today there are people who "take the law into their own hands" to avenge a wrong. With your class, cite some recent examples of this and discuss your feelings about such behaviour. What would be the consequences today?

4. Compare Hamlet's first response to the Ghost's call for revenge (lines 29–31) with his statement at the end of the scene (lines 190–191). How do you account for the differences between these two responses?

5. Write a brief e-mail exchange between Horatio and Marcellus on the subject of Hamlet's behaviour at the end of the scene.

Act 1: Consider the Whole Act

1. Divide the class into five groups. During the entire study of *Hamlet*, each group will be responsible for keeping track of a type of imagery. The imagery groups are:

   - Garden imagery
   - Disease, decay, and corruption imagery
   - Animal and hunting imagery
   - Images of pretence (for example, painting, cosmetics, acting)
   - Mythological allusions

   As you read the play, note the images that belong to your group's category. At the end of each Act, meet with your group and make a list of the images. Create an Imagery Wall in the class, including relevant quotations as well as visuals to illustrate them.

2. In this Act, you have seen Hamlet in a number of different situations and relationships. As a class or with your group, discuss the qualities that he reveals when he is in the presence of the following people: Gertrude, Claudius, Horatio, the Ghost. How do each of these people feel about Hamlet? After the discussion, in the role of one of these characters, write a diary entry about your concerns for Hamlet.

3. Create your own artistic expression of some of the important images in this Act. This can take the form of photographs, sketches, paintings, collages, or music. You may quote some images, e.g., "Look again as a teenager," and use them to develop your visual display.

4. Imagine that you are a palace photographer who has been able to take photographs that reveal a person's true nature, which is different from the way that person appears in public. With a camera, create photographs that reveal the true nature of Claudius, Hamlet, Polonius, Ophelia, and Gertrude. Your candid photographs may lead to a discussion of other themes in the play.

5. This Act contains some lines that have become famous on their own. Some examples are: "Something is rotten in the state of Denmark" (I, iv, 90); "Frailty they name is woman!" (I, ii, 146); "There are more things in heaven and earth, Horatio, / Than are dreamt of in (y)our philosophy" (I, v, 167–168); and "The time is out of joint" (I, v, 190). As a class, brainstorm some more quotations and suggest how they could be used as titles for essays or headlines for newspaper articles. Consider both humorous and serious topics.

6. As a class, watch a video or DVD of Act 1 and discuss these questions:

   - In what ways does a video or DVD version differ from one that is performed on a stage?

   - What feelings were created by the music, the costumes, and the sets?

   - How did the director highlight the contrasts between scenes and between characters?

   - Was there any part of the video or DVD performance that you would have directed or acted differently?

7. In your journal, write about a time in your life when you had to "act" a certain way, although your real feelings were very different. What effects did the pretending have on you and on your relationships with your friends or with your parents?

For the next scene . . .

If a parent is supporting a son or daughter living away from home, do you think the parent has the right to "check up" on the child's behaviour? If so, what methods of "checking up" would you consider acceptable or not acceptable? In your case, would it really affect your behaviour?

Act 2, Scene 1

In this scene . . .

Polonius dispatches his servant Reynaldo to Paris to deliver money to Laertes. At the same time, he coaches Reynaldo on different ways to spy on Laertes. Ophelia enters, upset and frightened, and tells Polonius about a disturbing visit she has just had from Hamlet. Hamlet's clothing was in disarray. Without speaking to Ophelia, he seemed to be painfully distancing from her. Polonius quickly concludes that Hamlet has gone mad because Ophelia rejected his love. He decides to inform the King immediately.

7	*Danskers:* Danes
8	*keep:* dwell, live

10	*By this . . . question:* by this method of indirect, casual questioning
11-12	*come you . . . touch it:* achieve your purpose better than you could by direct questioning. (Notice Polonius' personality and methods.)

19-20	*put on . . . please:* accuse him of any imagined faults you wish
20	*rank:* gross
22-24	*such wanton . . . liberty:* wild behaviour that is characteristic of young people who are on their own

24	*gaming:* gambling

26	*Drabbing:* associating with prostitutes
28	*season it in the charge:* make it sound less serious by the casual way you mention it

Act 2, Scene 1

A room in Polonius' house.
Enter Polonius and Reynaldo.

Polonius: Give him this money, and these notes, Reynaldo.
Reynaldo: I will, my lord.
Polonius: You shall do marvellous wisely, good Reynaldo,
   Before you visit him, to make inquiry
   Of his behaviour.
Reynaldo: My lord, I did intend it.   5
Polonius: Marry, well said, very well said. Look you, sir,
   Inquire me first what Danskers are in Paris,
   And how, and who, what means, and where they keep,
   What company, at what expense, and finding
   By this encompassment and drift of question   10
   That they do know my son, come you more nearer
   Than your particular demands will touch it:
   Take you, as 'twere, some distant knowledge of him,
   As thus, "I know his father, and his friends,
   And, in part, him"; do you mark this, Reynaldo?   15
Reynaldo: Ay, very well, my lord.
Polonius: "And, in part, him"; but, you may say, "not well
   But, if't be he I mean, he's very wild,
   Addicted so and so"; and there put on him
   What forgeries you please; marry, none so rank   20
   As may dishonour him; take heed of that;
   But, sir, such wanton, wild, and usual slips
   As are companions noted and most known
   To youth and liberty.
Reynaldo: As gaming, my lord.
Polonius: Ay, or drinking, fencing, swearing, quarrelling,   25
   Drabbing: you may go so far.
Reynaldo: My lord, that would dishonour him.
Polonius: Faith, no; as you may season it in the charge.
   You must not put another scandal on him,

30	*open to incontinency:* practising extreme habitual debauchery
31	*quaintly:* cleverly
32	*taints of liberty:* faults resulting from having too much freedom
35	*of general assault:* typical of young people

38	*fetch of warrant:* legitimate trick. (Obviously, Polonius believes that the end justifies the means.)
39	*sullies:* accusations of disgraceful behaviour
41	*Mark you:* pay attention
42	*Your party in converse:* the person you are talking to
43	*prenominate:* aforementioned
45	*closes . . . consequence:* agrees with you as follows
47	*addition:* title

58	*o'ertook in's rouse:* so drunk that he lost consciousness
61	*Videlicet:* (Latin) namely
63	*Your bait . . . truth:* By using lie as bait, you fish out the truth. (The carp was considered an easy fish to catch.)
64	*we . . . reach:* we who are wise and far-sighted
65	*With windlasses . . . bias:* through twists and indirect approaches

That he is open to incontinency;   30
That's not my meaning: but breathe his faults so quaintly
That they may seem the taints of liberty,
The flash and outbreak of a fiery mind,
A savageness in unreclaimed blood,
Of general assault.
Reynaldo: But, my good lord,—   35
Polonius: Wherefore should you do this?
Reynaldo: Ay, my lord,
I would know that.
Polonius: Marry, sir, here's my drift,
And I believe it is a fetch of warrant:
You laying these slight sullies on my son,
As 'twere a thing a little soil'd i' the working,   40
Mark you,
Your party in converse, him you would sound,
Having ever seen in the prenominate crimes
The youth you breathe of guilty, be assured
He closes with you in this consequence: 45
"Good sir," or so; or "friend," or "gentleman,"
According to the phrase or the addition
Of man and country.
Reynaldo: Very good, my lord.
Polonius: And then, sir, does he this—he does—
What was I about to say? By the mass, I was about to   50
    say something: where did I leave?
Reynaldo: At "closes in the consequence," at "friend, or
    so," and "gentleman."
Polonius: At "closes in the consequence," ay, marry;
He closes with you thus: "I know the gentleman;   55
I saw him yesterday, or t'other day,"
Or then, or then; with such or such, and, as you say,
"There was a gaming, there o'ertook in's rouse,
There falling out at tennis": or perchance,
"I saw him enter such a house of sale";   60
Videlicet, a brothel, or so forth.
See you now;
Your bait of falsehood takes this carp of truth:
And thus do we of wisdom and of reach,
With windlasses and with assays of bias,   65

66   *By indirections find directions out:* by indirect methods find out the truth

68   *You have me:* you understand me

73   *let him ply his music:* let him carry on as he wishes (i.e., Reynaldo should only find out about Laertes' behaviour, not correct it.)

79   *his doublet all unbraced:* his jacket completely open

80   *foul'd:* loose and twisted. The image is of an anchor's ropes.

81   *down-gyved to his ancle:* fallen down to his ankle. (In Elizabethan times, a man who wanted to show that he was in love would dress negligently.)

83   *purport:* meaning

91   *perusal:* study

By indirections find directions out:
So, by my former lecture and advice,
  Shall you my son. You have me, have you not?
Reynaldo: My lord, I have.
Polonius: God be wi'ye; fare ye well.
Reynaldo: Good, my lord.   70
Polonius: Observe his inclination in yourself.
Reynaldo: I shall, my lord.
Polonius: And let him ply his music.
Reynaldo: Well, my lord.

                                 [*Exit.*]

Polonius: Farewell!

[Enter Ophelia.]

  How now, Ophelia? what's the matter?   75
Ophelia: Alas, my lord, I have been so affrighted!
Polonius: With what, i' the name of heaven?
Ophelia: My lord, as I was sewing in my chamber,
  Lord Hamlet, with his doublet all unbraced,
  No hat upon his head, his stockings foul'd,   80
  Ungarter'd, and down-gyved to his ancle:
  Pale as his shirt, his knees knocking each other,
  And with a look so piteous in purport,
  As if he had been loosed out of hell
  To speak of horrors, he comes before me.   85
Polonius: Mad for thy love!
Ophelia: My lord, I do not know,
  But truly I do fear it.
Polonius: What said he?
Ophelia: He took me by the wrist and held me hard;
  Then goes he to the length of all his arm,
  And, with his other hand thus o'er his brow,   90
  He falls to such perusal of my face
  As he would draw it. Long stay'd he so;
  At last, a little shaking of mine arm,
  And thrice his head thus waving up and down,
  He raised a sigh so piteous and profound   95
  That it did seem to shatter all his bulk
  And end his being: that done, he lets me go:
  And with his head over his shoulder turn'd,

103   *ecstasy:* madness
104   *fordoes:* destroys

112   *access:* admittance

114   *quoted:* observed
115   *jealousy:* suspicion
116-119 *By heaven . . . discretion:* It is just as natural for old men to be overly suspicious as it is for the young to be indiscreet.

120-121 *This must . . . love:* Hamlet's love (or madness) must be reported to the King. To keep it secret might cause more harm than it would to tell about it, which might cause anger.

He seem'd to find his way without his eyes;
For out o' doors he went without their helps,   100
And to the last bended their light on me.
Polonius: Come, go with me; I will go seek the king.
This is the very ecstasy of love;
Whose violent property fordoes itself
And leads the will to desperate undertakings   105
As oft as any passion under heaven
That does afflict our natures. I am sorry.
What, have you given him any hard words of late?
Ophelia: No, my good lord; but, as you did command,
I did repel his letters and denied   110
His access to me.
Polonius: That hath made him mad.
I am sorry that with better heed and judgment
I had not quoted him: I fear'd he did but trifle
And meant to wreck thee; but beshrew my jealousy! 115
By heaven it is as proper to our age
To cast beyond ourselves in our opinions
As it is common for the younger sort
To lack discretion. Come, go we to the king:
This must be known; which, being kept close, might move 120
More grief to hide than hate to utter love.
Come.   [*Exeunt.*]

Act 2, Scene 1: Activities

1. In pairs, write point-form notes that Polonius might have made before his conversation with Reynaldo. In your group, summarize Polonius' instructions to Reynaldo. Then prepare a soliloquy that Reynaldo would deliver to the audience after receiving Polonius' instructions. Perform the soliloquy for the class, and compare it with the soliloques of your classmates.

2. Ophelia's report about Hamlet's strange clothing and behaviour conforms to the sixteenth-century Elizabethan image of a "mad lover." In your group, discuss how people who are "crazy in love" are portrayed nowadays in movies, television, or music videos.

3. The illustration at the beginning of this scene (opposite page 81) is like a tableau. A tableau is a frozen picture, where the characters are caught in mid-action. Their facial expressions and gestures reveal their personality, emotions, and relationships. In your group, create the following tableaux:

   - Polonius giving instructions to Reynaldo
   - Hamlet's encounter with Ophelia
   - Ophelia telling Polonius about the encounter with Hamlet

   Present some tableaux to the class, and compare them with other groups' tableaux.

4. Hamlet has adopted an "antic disposition" as part of his secret plan to take revenge on Claudius. In your group, suggest how an antic disposition might help Hamlet in his plan and how it might not. After weighing the pros and cons, present your opinion of Hamlet's plan to the class. As the play unfolds, you will be able to take note of how this plan works out.

5. In your group, write short items for a gossip column about Elsinore's "rich and famous" residents. Update your readers on Gertrude and Claudius, the Polonius family,

Hamlet, and the relationship between Hamlet and Ophelia. Write headlines for these items to spark the curiosity of your readers. Share your tabloid journalism with the class.

6. In your group, discuss Polonius' personality as revealed in this scene. Discuss whether or not you would consider him to be a role model as a parent or as a court adviser. Report your group's opinion to the class, with reasons.

7. As a friend who has heard about Ophelia's encounter with Hamlet, write her a letter of advice.

For the next scene . . .

Suppose your close friend has been acting very strangely. Your friend's parents ask you to find out the reasons for the strange mood and then report back to them. Under what circumstances would you be willing to do this? How would you feel about this request? Would you tell your friend what you were doing?

Act 2, Scene 2
In this scene . . .

Two months have passed. Two old friends of Hamlet, Rosencrantz and Guildenstern, have been summoned to the palace by Claudius and Gertrude, who ask them to spy on Hamlet. Polonius enters and announces the return of the two ambassadors sent to Norway, who bring news that the military threat from Norway has been resolved. Polonius then tells Claudius and Gertrude that he knows the cause of Hamlet's apparent madness: Ophelia has rejected his love. He offers to arrange an "accidental" meeting between Hamlet and Ophelia so that he and Claudius can spy on their conversation. Hamlet enters, reading a book. Polonius makes conversation with him, and Hamlet replies quite irrationally; however, Polonius recognizes that there is truth buried in Hamlet's mad words. Hamlet then greets Rosencrantz and Guildenstern warmly, but he soon realizes they are on a spying mission. When he tells them how depressed he is, they try to cheer him up with news about some travelling actors visiting the court. Hamlet greets the players warmly and asks the lead actor to insert an extra few lines into the play *The Murder of Gonzago*, to be performed before the King the next night. In a soliloquy, Hamlet chastises himself for delaying the revenge of his father's murder. No longer certain that the Ghost was sincere, Hamlet will test Claudius' guilt by watching his reaction to a play in which old King Hamlet's murder will be re-enacted.

2   *Moreover that:* over and above the fact that

3   *provoke:* cause

11   *of so young days:* from such a young age

12   *sith:* since; *neighbour'd to:* close to

13   *vouchsafe your rest:* consent to stay

18   *open'd:* if it were revealed

21   *To whom . . . adheres:* to whom he is more partial or loyal

22   *gentry:* gentlemanliness, courtesy

24   *For the supply and profit of our hope:* to help fulfill our hope (of finding the cause of Hamlet's disturbance)

Scene 2

A room in the castle.
Enter King, Queen, Rosencrantz,
Guildenstern, and Attendants

King: Welcome, dear Rosencrantz and Guildenstern!
　　Moreover that we much did long to see you,
　　The need we have to use you did provoke
　　Our hasty sending. Something have you heard
　　Of Hamlet's transformation; so I call it,　　　　　　5
　　Since not the exterior nor the inward man
　　Resembles that it was. What it should be,
　　More than his father's death, that thus hath put him
　　So much from the understanding of himself,
　　I cannot deem of: I entreat you both,　　　　　　　10
　　That, being of so young days brought up with him
　　And sith so neighbour'd to his youth and haviour,
　　That you vouchsafe your rest here in our court
　　Some little time: so by your companies
　　To draw him on to pleasures, and to gather,　　　　15
　　So much as from occasion you may glean,
　　Whether aught to us unknown afflicts him thus,
　　That open'd lies within our remedy.
Queen: Good gentlemen, he hath much talk'd of you,
　　And sure I am two men there are not living　　　　　20
　　To whom he more adheres. If it will please you
　　To show us so much gentry and good will,
　　As to expend your time with us a while
　　For the supply and profit of our hope,
　　Your visitation shall receive such thanks　　　　　　25
　　As fits a king's remembrance.
Rosencrantz:　　　　　　　　　　　Both your majesties
　　Might, by the sovereign power you have of us,
　　Put your dread pleasures more into command
　　Than to entreaty.
Guildenstern:　　　　　But we both obey,

30	*in the full bent:* to the utmost. The image is of a bow stretched to the limit before the arrow is loosed.
38	*practices:* actions. The word "practices" was also used to mean "tricks."
42	*still:* always
44-45	*I hold my duty . . . king:* I consider my duty to my king as important as my duty to God.
47	*Hunts not the trail of policy so sure:* doesn't follow or track the methods of statecraft (politics) as well
52	*fruit to that great feast:* the dessert (the sweetest, best part)
55	*distemper:* disturbed state of mind
56	*doubt:* suspect; *main:* chief point
58	*sift:* question closely
60	*desires:* good wishes

And here give up ourselves, in the full bent   30
   To lay our service freely at your feet,
   To be commanded.
King: Thanks, Rosencrantz and gentle Guildenstern.
Queen: Thanks, Guildenstern and gentle Rosencrantz:
   And I beseech you instantly to visit   35
   My too much changed son. Go, some of you,
   And bring these gentlemen where Hamlet is.
Guildenstern: Heavens make our presence and our practices
   Pleasant and helpful to him!
Queen: Ay, amen!

   [Exeunt Rosencrantz, Guildenstern, and some Attendants.]

   [Enter Polonius.]

Polonius: The ambassadors from Norway, my good lord,   40
   Are joyfully return'd.
King: Thou still hast been the father of good news.
Polonius: Have I, my lord? Assure you my good liege,
   I hold my duty as I hold my soul,
   Both to my God and to my gracious king: 45
   And I do think, or else this brain of mine
   Hunts not the trail of policy so sure
   As it hath used to do, that I have found
   The very cause of Hamlet's lunacy.
King: O, speak of that; that do I long to hear.   50
Polonius: Give first admittance to the ambassadors;
   My news shall be the fruit to that great feast.
King: Thyself do grace to them, and bring them in.
                        [Exit Polonius.]
   He tells me, my dear Gertrude, that he hath found
   The head and source of all your son's distemper.   55
Queen: I doubt it is no other but the main;
   His father's death, and our o'erhasty marriage.
King: Well, we shall sift him.

   [Re-enter Polonius, with Voltimand and Cornelius.]

                   Welcome, my good friends!
   Say, Voltimand, what from our brother Norway?
Voltimand: Most fair return of greetings and desires.   60

61   *Upon our first:* as a result of our first conference

67   *falsely borne in hand:* deceived; *sends out arrests:* sends
          out commands (for Fortinbras) to stop his operations
69   *in fine:* in short

71   *To give . . . arms:* to test out his military strength

79-80   *On such regards . . . set down:* The document sets out the
          conditions whereby the Norwegian army will be allowed to
          pass through Denmark without posing a threat.
80   *It likes us well:* It pleases us

86-92   Polonius' speech is an example of the very thing he is criti-
          cizing. This type of humour is called satire. Shakespeare
          often pokes fun in this way at people whose speech is full
          of flourishes, but whose message is not clear.
90   *wit:* understanding
91   *outward flourishes:* display of fine clothing

Upon our first, he sent out to suppress
His nephew's levies; which to him appear'd
To be a preparation 'gainst the Polack,
But better look'd into, he truly found
It was against your highness: whereat, grieved,　　　　65
That so his sickness, age, and impotence
Was falsely borne in hand, sends out arrests
On Fortinbras; which he, in brief, obeys,
Receives rebuke from Norway, and in fine
Makes vow before his uncle never more　　　　70
To give the assay of arms against your majesty.
Whereon old Norway, overcome with joy,
Gives him three thousand crowns in annual fee
And his commission to employ those soldiers,
So levied as before, against the Polack:　　　　75
With an entreaty, herein further shown,
　　　　　　　　　　　　　[*Gives a paper.*]
That it might please you to give quiet pass
Through your dominions for his enterprise,
On such regards of safety and allowance
As therein are set down.
King:　　　　　　　　It likes us well,　　　　80
And, at our more consider'd time, we'll read,
Answer, and think upon this business.
Meantime we thank you for your well-took labour:
Go to your rest; at night we'll feast together:
Most welcome home!
　　　　　　[*Exeunt Voltimand and Cornelius.*]
Polonius:　　　　　　This business is well ended.　　　　85
My liege, and madam, to expostulate
What majesty should be, what duty is,
Why day is day, night night, and time is time,
Were nothing but to waste night, day, and time.
Therefore, since brevity is the soul of wit　　　　90
And tediousness the limbs and outward flourishes,
I will be brief. Your noble son is mad:
Mad call I it: for, to define true madness,
What is't, but to be nothing else but mad?
But let that go.
Queen:　　　　　　More matter, with less art.　　　　95

98   *figure:* that is, figure of speech

105   *Perpend:* Consider (a pedantic word, unsuitable for this conversation)

110   *That's an ill phrase:* Polonius is referring to the word "beautified," which he finds artificial.

112   *In her . . . bosom:* for her eyes and heart alone

119   *ill at these numbers:* untalented at writing rhyme

120   *reckon:* count

122   *machine:* body

Polonius: Madam, I swear I use no art at all.
 That he is mad 'tis true: 'tis true 'tis pity,
 And pity 'tis 'tis true: a foolish figure;
 But farewell it, for I will use no art.
 Mad let us grant him then: and now remains   100
 That we find out the cause of this effect,
 Or rather say, the cause of this defect,
 For this effect defective comes by cause:
 Thus it remains, and the remainder thus.
 Perpend.   105
 I have a daughter, have while she is mine,—
 Who in her duty and obedience, mark,
 Hath given me this: now gather, and surmise.

 [*Reads.*] To the celestial, and my soul's idol, the most
  beautified Ophelia.—

 That's an ill phrase, a vile phrase; "beautified" is a vile   110
  phrase: but you shall hear. Thus:

 In her excellent white bosom, these, etc.

Queen: Came this from Hamlet to her?
Polonius: Good madam, stay a while; I will be faithful.
               [*Reads.*]

 Doubt thou the stars are fire;   115
  Doubt that the sun doth move;
 Doubt truth to be a liar;
  But never doubt I love.

 O dear Ophelia, I am ill at these numbers; I have
  not art to reckon my groans; but that I love thee   120
  best, O most best, believe it. Adieu.
 Thine evermore, most dear lady, whilst this machine
  is to him. *Hamlet.*

 This in obedience hath my daughter showed me:
 And more above, hath his solicitings,
 As they fell out by time, by means and place,   125
 All given to mine ear.
King: But how hath she
 Received his love?

129   *fain:* willingly

134   *If I . . . table-book:* If I had acted as go-between, passing
        communications back and forth. (The desk or the book
        would both be places where a message could be left);
        table-book: memorandum book

135   *given my heart a winking:* pretended to ignore

136   *idle sight:* indifference

139   *out of thy star:* far above you. The reference is to the belief
        that every star moved within its own sphere and could not
        travel beyond it.

140   *prescripts:* orders

141   *resort:* access

143   *took the fruits:* benefited from

146   *watch:* insomnia

147   *lightness:* lightheadedness; *declension:* deterioration

157   *centre:* the centre of the earth (i.e., the most inaccessible
        place)

160   *loose:* The use of "loose" emphasizes Ophelia's passivity
        and powerlessness. It suggests a number of images such
        as letting a dog off a leash, releasing an animal as bait in a
        hunt, or even sending animals to mate.

161   *arras:* a tapestry hanging, made in Arras, France

Polonius: What do you think of me?
King: As of a man faithful and honourable.
Polonius: I would fain prove so. But what might you think
   When I had seen this hot love on the wing,— 130
   As I perceived it, I must tell you that,
   Before my daughter told me—what might you,
   Or my dear majesty your queen here, think,
   If I had play'd the desk or table-book,
   Or given my heart a winking, mute and dumb, 135
   Or look'd upon this love with idle sight;
   What might you think? No, I went round to work,
   And my young mistress thus I did bespeak:
   "Lord Hamlet is a prince out of thy star;
   This must not be"; and then I prescripts gave her 140
   That she should lock herself from his resort,
   Admit no messengers, receive no tokens.
   Which done, she took the fruits of my advice;
   And he repulsed, a short tale to make,
   Fell into a sadness, then into a fast, 145
   Thence to a watch, thence into a weakness,
   Thence to a lightness, and by this declension
   Into the madness whereon now he raves
   And all we mourn for.
King: Do you think this?
Queen: It may be, very like. 150
Polonius: Hath there been such a time, I'd fain know that,
   That I have positively said, 'tis so,
   When it proved otherwise?
King: Not that I know.
Polonius: Take this from this, if this be otherwise:
             [*Pointing to his head and shoulder.*]
   If circumstances lead me, I will find 155
   Where truth is hid, though it were hid indeed
   Within the centre.
King: How may we try it further?
Polonius: You know, sometimes he walks four hours together
   Here in the lobby.
Queen: So he does, indeed.
Polonius: At such a time I'll loose my daughter to him: 160
   Be you and I behind an arras then;

168   *board:* accost, address

170   *God-a-mercy:* God have mercy, or thank God

172   *fishmonger:* a fishseller (also used to mean "pimp")

179   Maggots were thought to be created by the sun (probably because they seem to appear out of nowhere in anything out in the sun). The phrase also echoes the ancient idea that the sun can create new life.

179-180   *being a god kissing carrion:* Even the sun-god can produce only maggots because of the corruption (carrion) he encounters.

181-182   *Let her not walk i' the sun:* The sun is associated with royalty. Therefore, Hamlet is warning Polonius to keep Ophelia out of the dangerous presence of either himself or the King.

189   *extremity:* pain, pangs

192   *What is the matter?:* What is the subject?

193   *Between who?:* Hamlet is deliberately misinterpreting the question.

195-203   Hamlet may be pretending to read this insulting description of old age, thus seizing an opportunity to insult Polonius.

197   *amber:* the gummy resin of evergreen trees

Mark the encounter; if he love her not,
And be not from his reason fallen thereon,
Let me be no assistant for a state,
And keep a farm and carters.
King: We will try it.   165
Queen: But look where sadly the poor wretch comes reading.
Polonius: Away, I do beseech you, both away!
    I'll board him presently.
                        [Exeunt King, Queen, and Attendants.]

[Enter Hamlet, reading.]

    O, give me leave, how does my good lord Hamlet?
Hamlet: Well, God-a-mercy.   170
Polonius: Do you know me, my lord?
Hamlet: Excellent well; you are a fishmonger.
Polonius: Not I, my lord.
Hamlet: Then I would you were so honest a man.
Polonius: Honest, my lord?   175
Hamlet: Ay, sir; to be honest, as this world goes, is to be
    one man picked out of ten thousand.
Polonius: That's very true, my lord.
Hamlet: For if the sun breed maggots in a dead dog, being
    a god kissing carrion—Have you a daughter?   180
Polonius: I have, my lord.
Hamlet: Let her not walk i' the sun. Conception is a blessing,
    but not as your daughter may conceive—friend look
    to't.
Polonius [Aside]: How say you by that? Still harping on my   185
    daughter; yet he knew me not at first; he said I was
    a fishmonger: he is far gone, far gone: and truly in my
    youth I suffered much extremity for love; very near
    this, I'll speak to him again.—What do you read, my
    lord?   190
Hamlet: Words, words, words!
Polonius: What is the matter, my lord?
Hamlet: Between who?
Polonius: I mean the matter that you read, my lord.
Hamlet: Slanders, sir; for the satirical rogue says here that   195
    old men have grey beards, that their faces are
    wrinkled, their eyes purging thick amber and plumtree

199   *hams:* thighs, buttocks

201   *honesty:* proper, fair behaviour

205   *method:* meaning, sense

207   *pregnant:* full of meaning, quick-witted
208   *happiness:* aptness of expression

211   *suddenly:* immediately

223   Notice the quick change in Hamlet's behaviour.

226   *indifferent:* average

228   *not the very button:* not the highest point (on the cap);
        therefore, not blessed with great fortune

233   *privates:* Guildenstern is punning on the word "privates,"
        meaning private parts of the body, and ordinary people
        (without rank).

gum, and that they have a plentiful lack of wit,
together with weak hams: all which, sir, though I most
powerfully and potently believe, yet I hold it not   200
honesty to have it thus set down; for yourself, sir, shall
grow old as I am, if, like a crab you could go
backward.

Polonius [*Aside*]: Though this be madness, yet there is
method in't.—Will you walk out of the air, my lord?   205

Hamlet: Into my grave?

Polonius: Indeed, that's out o' the air. [*Aside.*] How pregnant
sometimes his replies are! a happiness that often
madness hits on, which reason and sanity could not so
prosperously be delivered of. I will leave him, and   210
suddenly contrive the means of meeting between him
and my daughter.—My honourable lord, I will
humbly take my leave of you.

Hamlet: You cannot, sir, take from me anything that I will
more willingly part withal, except my life, except my   215
life, except my life.

Polonius: Fare you well, my lord.

Hamlet: These tedious old fools!

   [*Enter Rosencrantz and Guildenstern.*]

Polonius: You go to seek the lord Hamlet; there he is.

Rosencrantz [*To Polonius*]: God save you, sir!   220

                        [*Exit Polonius.*]

Guildenstern: Mine honoured lord!

Rosencrantz: My most dear lord!

Hamlet: My excellent good friends! How dost thou,
Guildenstern! Ah, Rosencrantz! Good lads, how do
you both?   225

Rosencrantz: As the indifferent children of the earth.

Guildenstern: Happy, in that we are not over happy;
On Fortune's cap we are not the very button.

Hamlet: Nor the soles of her shoes?

Rosencrantz: Neither, my lord.   230

Hamlet: Then you live about her waist or in the middle of
her favours?

Guildenstern: Faith, her privates we.

Hamlet: In the secret parts of fortune? O most true; she is

235   *strumpet:* prostitute (Fortune is a strumpet because she cannot be relied upon for continued favours; she is fickle.)

238   *doomsday:* Day of Judgment. Hamlet is cynically suggesting that if people are honest, it must be because the end of the world is near.

243   *prison:* Hamlet may be referring to the King's request that he not return to Wittenberg. Also, the feeling of being in prison was considered a symptom of melancholy.

245   *confines:* places of imprisonment

252   *ambition:* Rosencrantz is trying to establish the cause of Hamlet's strange behaviour by testing the idea that he is unhappy because his ambition to be king has been thwarted.

256   *bad dreams:* another symptom of melancholy or depression

263-264 *Then are . . . shadows:* If a king or a hero is a mere shadow because he is ambitious, then a beggar (the opposite of a king) must be the body (the opposite of a shadow) and, therefore, more substantial than a king. Hamlet has constructed a clever argument from Rosencrantz and Guildenstern's word-play that both ridicules and puts an end to it.

265   *fay:* faith

267   *sort:* classify

269   *dreadfully attended:* poorly served

269-270 *in the beaten way of friendship:* speaking openly as one friend to another

270   *what make you:* what are you doing

a strumpet. What's the news? 235

Rosencrantz: None, my lord; but that the world's grown
honest.

Hamlet: Then is doomsday near: but your news is not true.
Let me question more in particular: what have you,
my good friends, deserved at the hands of Fortune, that 240
she sends you to prison hither?

Guildenstern: Prison, my lord!

Hamlet: Denmark's a prison.

Rosencrantz: Then is the world one.

Hamlet: A goodly one; in which there are many confines, 245
wards, and dungeons, Denmark being one o'the
worst.

Rosencrantz: We think not so, my lord.

Hamlet: Why, then, 'tis none to you: for there is nothing
either good or bad but thinking makes it so: to me it 250
is a prison.

Rosencrantz: Why, then your ambition makes it one; 'tis
too narrow for your mind.

Hamlet: O God, I could be bounded in a nut-shell, and count
myself a king of infinite space, were it not that I have 255
bad dreams.

Guildenstern: Which dreams indeed are ambition; for the
very substance of the ambitious is merely the shadow
of a dream.

Hamlet: A dream itself is but a shadow. 260

Rosencrantz: Truly, and I hold ambition of so airy and light
a quality that it is but a shadow's shadow.

Hamlet: Then are our beggars bodies, and our monarchs
and outstretched heroes the beggars' shadows. Shall we
to the court? for, by my fay, I cannot reason. 265

Rosencrantz, Guildenstern: We'll wait upon you.

Hamlet: No such matter: I will not sort you with the rest
of my servants; for, to speak to you like an honest man,
I am most dreadfully attended. But, in the beaten way
of friendship, what make you at Elsinore? 270

Rosencrantz: To visit you, my lord; no other occasion.

Hamlet: Beggar that I am, I am even poor in thanks; but I
thank you: and sure, dear friends, my thanks are too
dear a halfpenny. Were you not sent for? Is it your own

280   *colour:* disguise, camouflage

283   *conjure:* command

284   *consonancy:* good companionship

293-294   *I will tell . . . discovery:* I will tell you why you have been sent to spy on me. That way you won't be in any danger of revealing your secret.

295   *moult no feather:* remain whole

296   *foregone all custom of exercises:* given up customary exercises

297-298   *it goes so heavily with my disposition:* I am so depressed

299   *a sterile promontory:* a barren headland jutting into the sea; *canopy:* covering

300   *brave:* glorious

301   *fretted:* adorned

302-303   *foul and pestilent congregation of vapours:* oppressive, poisonous fog

303   *piece of work:* work of artistic creation

304   *faculty:* intelligence

305   *express:* fitted to the purpose

306   *apprehension:* understanding

307   *paragon:* ideal, model

308   *quintessence:* basic element that remains after other components have been removed. The image is taken from alchemy; the quintessence of a substance would be all that was left once it had been purged of earth, air, water and fire (the four elements believed to make up all matter).

inclining? Is it a free visitation? Come, deal justly with   275
    me: come, come; nay, speak.
Guildenstern: What should we say, my lord?
Hamlet: Why, anything, but to the purpose. You were sent
    for; and there is a kind of confession in your looks,
    which your modesties have not craft enough to colour: 280
    I know the good king and queen have sent for you.
Rosencrantz: To what end, my lord?
Hamlet: That you must teach me. But let me conjure you,
    by the rights of our fellowship, by the consonancy
    of our youth, by the obligation of our ever-preserved   285
    love, and by what more dear a better proposer could
    charge you withal, be even and direct with me,
    whether you were sent for, or no?
Rosencrantz [*Aside to Guildenstern*]: What say you?
Hamlet [*Aside*]: Nay then, I have an eye of you: if you love   290
    me, hold not off.
Guildenstern: My lord, we were sent for.
Hamlet: I will tell you why; so shall my anticipation prevent
    your discovery, and your secrecy to the king and
    queen moult no feather. I have of late—but wherefore   295
    I know not—lost all my mirth, forgone all custom of
    exercises: and indeed it goes so heavily with my
    disposition that this goodly frame, the earth, seems to
    me a sterile promontory; this most excellent canopy,
    the air, look you, this brave o'erhanging firmament, this 300
    majestical roof fretted with golden fire, why, it appears
    no other thing to me than a foul and pestilent
    congregation of vapours. What a piece of work is a
    man! how noble in reason! how infinite in faculty! in
    form and moving how express and admirable! in   305
    action how like an angel! in apprehension how like a
    god! the beauty of the world! the paragon of animals!
    And yet, to me, what is this quintessence of dust?
    man delights not me: no, nor woman neither, though
    by your smiling you seem to say so.   310
Rosencrantz: My lord, there was no such stuff in my
    thoughts.
Hamlet: Why did you laugh then, when I said, "man delights
    not me"?

| 316 | *lenten:* poor, meagre. (Lent is a season of fasting.) |
| 317 | *coted:* passed |

321	*foil and target:* sword and shield
322	*the humorous man:* the man who is governed by humours or moods, especially those tending to violent rages
319-325	Hamlet is cataloguing the typical acting roles of Shakespeare's time. From this point until line 360, Shakespeare abandons the time and place of the play to make references to the theatre of his day.
323-324	*tickled o' the sere:* easily moved to laughter. The image is of a gun easily set off by the trigger (sere).
326	*were wont to:* were accustomed to
326-360	These lines describe London theatre politics current in Shakespeare's time. The main features were the popularity of child actors and the war of words between companies of child actors and those of adult actors.

337	*eyrie:* brood (of birds), group. Shakespeare is referring to a group of child actors who began performing in 1600; *eyases:* (noisy) young birds, nestlings
338	*on the top of question:* noisily, drowning out other voices
338-339	*tyrannically clapped:* loudly applauded (so that nothing else can be heard)
340	*berattle the common stages:* satirize, make fun of the regular theatres
341	*many wearing . . . goose-quills:* sword-carrying noblemen are afraid of the (written) ridicule that the actors direct at them
344	*escoted:* paid; *pursue the quality:* follow the profession
344-345	*no longer . . . sing:* until their voices crack
348-349	*exclaim . . . succession:* make fun of what they themselveswill one day become (i.e., adult actors)
351	*tarre:* incite
352-354	*there was . . . question:* The only profitable plays were those in which children's acting troupes and adult acting troupes ridiculed each other.

Rosencrantz: To think, my lord, if you delight not in man,　315
　　what lenten entertainment the players shall receive
　　from you: we coted them on the way; and hither are
　　they coming, to offer you service.

Hamlet: He that plays the king shall be welcome; his majesty
　　shall have tribute of me: the adventurous knight shall　320
　　use his foil and target: the lover shall not sigh gratis;
　　the humorous man shall end his part in peace: the clown
　　shall make those laugh whose lungs are tickled o' the
　　sere; and the lady shall say her mind freely, or the blank
　　verse shall halt for't. What players are they?　325

Rosencrantz: Even those you were wont to take delight in,
　　the tragedians of the city.

Hamlet: How chances it they travel? their residence, both
　　in reputation and profit, was better both ways.

Rosencrantz: I think their inhibition comes by the means of　330
　　the late innovation.

Hamlet: Do they hold the same estimation they did when I
　　was in the city? Are they so followed?

Rosencrantz: No, indeed, they are not.

Hamlet: How comes it? Do they grow rusty?　335

Rosencrantz: Nay, their endeavour keeps in the wonted pace:
　　but there is, sir, an eyrie of children, little eyases, that
　　cry out on the top of question and are most tyrannically
　　clapped for't: these are now the fashion, and so
　　berattle the common stages,—so they call them,—that　340
　　many wearing rapiers are afraid of goose-quills, and
　　dare scarce come thither.

Hamlet: What, are they children? who maintains 'em? how
　　are they escoted? Will they pursue the quality no
　　longer than they can sing? will they not say afterwards,　345
　　if they should grow themselves to common players,—
　　as it is most like, if their means are no better,—their
　　writers do them wrong, to make them exclaim against
　　their own succession?

Rosencrantz: Faith, there has been much to do on both sides,　350
　　and the nation holds it no sin, to tarre them to
　　controversy: there was for a while no money bid for
　　argument unless the poet and the player went to cuffs
　　in the question.

358   *carry it away:* win

359-360   *Hercules and his load:* The sign of the Globe Theatre showed Hercules carrying the globe. Hence, it seems that even Shakespeare's theatre suffered from the popularity of the child actors.

361-366   Hamlet compares the new admiration for the child actors to the admiration for the new king – hinting that there is little justification for either.

362   *make mowes:* make faces

364   *ducats:* gold coins; *his picture in little:* a miniature picture, usually worn on a chain; *'Sblood:* God's blood

369   *the appurtenance of welcome:* the proper behaviour that goes with a welcome

371-372   *comply . . . garb:* behave with formal politeness

372   *extent:* behaviour

376-377   *I am . . . handsaw:* Hamlet is saying that his madness depends on the weather, and that he is mad only some of the time; *I know a hawk from a handsaw:* I can distinguish one thing from another. "Handsaw" is a corruption of "hernshaw" (heron). Hawks were used to hunt herons. Thus, Hamlet is hinting that he can recognize his enemies.

381   *swathing clouts:* baby clothes

382   *Happily:* perhaps

388   *Roscius:* a famous Roman actor in Julius Caesar's time

Hamlet: Is't possible? 355
Guildenstern: O, there has been much throwing about of
    brains.
Hamlet: Do the boys carry it away?
Rosencrantz: Ay, that they do, my lord; Hercules and his
    load too. 360
Hamlet: It is not very strange; for mine uncle is king of
    Denmark, and those that would make mowes at him
    while my father lived, give twenty, forty, an hundred
    ducats a-piece, for his picture in little. 'Sblood, there
    is something in this more than natural, if philosophy 365
    could find it out.

                            [Flourish of trumpets without.]

Guildenstern: There are the players.
Hamlet: Gentlemen, you are welcome to Elsinore. Your
    hands, come then: the appurtenance of welcome is
    fashion and ceremony: let me comply with you in the 370
    garb, lest my extent to the players, which, I tell you,
    must show fairly outwards, should more appear like
    entertainment than yours. You are welcome: but my
    uncle-father and aunt-mother are deceived.
Guildenstern: In what, my dear lord? 375
Hamlet: I am but mad north-north-west: when the wind is
    southerly I know a hawk from a handsaw.

[Enter Polonius.]

Polonius: Well be with you, gentlemen!
Hamlet: Hark you, Guildenstern; and you too; at each ear
    a hearer: that great baby you see there is not yet out of 380
    his swathing clouts.
Rosencrantz: Happily he's the second time come to them;
    for they say an old man is twice a child.
Hamlet: I will prophesy he comes to tell me of the players;
    mark it. You say right, sir: o' Monday morning; 'twas 385
    so, indeed.
Polonius: My lord, I have news to tell you.
Hamlet: My lord, I have news to tell you. When Roscius
    was an actor in Rome,—
Polonius: The actors are come hither, my lord. 390
Hamlet: Buz, buz!

394-397   a catalogue of different dramatic genres of Shakespeare's time

397-398   *Seneca . . . Plautus:* two great Roman playwrights

398-399   *the law . . . liberty:* the rules of classical drama or the looser forms (such as Shakespeare's own plays)

400   *Jephthah:* Jephthah is a character in the Bible who sacrificed his daughter to fulfill an oath (Judges 11:30–40). Is Hamlet trying to make Polonius nervous about Ophelia?

416   *row:* stanza; *chanson:* ballad

417   *abridgment:* entertainment; also, interruption

420   *valiant:* bearded (a beard was a symbol of valour)

421-422   *my young lady:* women's roles were played by boys

424   *chopine:* an overshoe with a high-corked sole

425   *cracked within the ring:* Hamlet is comparing a boy's cracked voice to a ruined coin. (A coin that had been chipped or shaved past the ring encircling the King's head was no longer legal currency.)

Polonius: Upon mine honour,—
Hamlet: Then came each actor on his ass,—
Polonius: The best actors in the world, either for tragedy, comedy, history, pastoral, pastoral-comical, historical- 395 pastoral, tragical-historical, tragical-comical-historical- pastoral, scene individable, or poem unlimited: Seneca cannot be too heavy, nor Plautus too light. For the law of writ and the liberty, these are the only men.
Hamlet: O Jephthah, judge of Israel, what a treasure hadst 400 thou!
Polonius: What a treasure had he, my lord?
Hamlet: Why—

One fair daughter and no more,
The which he loved passing well. 405

Polonius [*Aside*]: Still on my daughter.
Hamlet: Am I not i' the right, old Jephthah?
Polonius: If you call me Jephthah, my lord, I have a daughter that I love passing well.
Hamlet: Nay, that follows not. 410
Polonius: What follows then, my lord?
Hamlet: Why,

As by lot, God wot

and then you know,

It came to pass, as most like it was. 415

The first row of the pious chanson will show you more: for look, where my abridgment comes.

[Enter Four or Five Players.]

You are welcome, masters; welcome, all. I am glad to see thee well. Welcome, good friends. O, my old friend! Why thy face is valiant since I saw thee last; 420 comest thou to beard me in Denmark? What, my young lady and mistress! By'r-lady, your ladyship is nearer to heaven than when I saw you last, by the altitude of a chopine. Pray God, your voice, like a piece of uncurrent gold, be not cracked within the ring. Masters, 425 you are all welcome. We'll e'en to't like French

428	*straight:* right away

433-434	*'twas caviare to the general:* It was too good for average audiences.
435-436	*cried in the top of mine:* was better than mine
436	*digested:* structured

438	*sallets:* spicy comments

440	*indict . . . affectation:* cause the author to be accused of being affected

443	*Aeneas' tale to Dido:* Aeneas survived the fall of Troy and eventually founded Rome. Dido was a Carthaginian queen Aeneas made love to and then abandoned.
444	*Priam:* King of Troy
447-515	The Player's speech recounts an episode from the Trojan War, which is roughly based on the version found in Virgil's *Aeneid.* The Player describes the murder of the old Trojan king, Priam, by Pyrrhus, son of Achilles. Following this is a description of Queen Hecuba's mourning over the slaughter of her husband Priam. The speech provides an interesting counterpart to the main plot of *Hamlet,* with its elements of murder of a king and the grief-stricken reaction of the Queen.
447	*Pyrrhus:* Achilles' son. He killed Priam when Troy fell; *Hyrcanian beast:* the tiger (the embodiment of cruelty)
451	*ominous horse:* the huge wooden horse the Greeks used to steal into Troy. It was "ominous" because it brought about Troy's doom.
454	*gules:* red (a term for heraldry; here it refers to blood)
456	*the parching streets:* The streets of Troy were on fire.
459	*o'er-sized:* stiffened with its covering (Sizing is used to stiffen cloth.)
460	*carbuncles:* red gemstones (garnets)

falconers, fly at anything we see: we'll have a speech
straight: come, give us a taste of your quality; come, a
passionate speech.
First Player: What speech, my lord?   430
Hamlet: I heard thee speak me a speech once, but it was
   never acted; or, if it was, not above once; for the play,
   I remember, pleased not the million; 'twas caviare to
   the general: but it was—as I received it, and others,
   whose judgment in such matters cried in the top of   435
   mine—an excellent play, well digested in the scenes,
   set down with as much modesty as cunning. I remember
   one said there were no sallets in the lines to make the
   matter savoury, nor no matter in the phrase that might
   indict the author of affectation; but called it an honest   440
   method, as wholesome as sweet, and by very much more
   handsome than fine. One speech in it I chiefly loved:
   'twas Æneas' tale to Dido; and thereabout of it
   especially, where he speaks of Priam's slaughter: if it
   live in your memory, begin at this line; let me see,   445
   let me see—

      The rugged Pyrrhus, like th' Hyrcanian beast.

It is not so; it begins with "Pyrrhus."
   The rugged Pyrrhus, he whose sable arms,
   Black as his purpose, did the night resemble   450
   When he lay couched in the ominous horse,
   Hath now this dread and black complexion smear'd
   With heraldry more dismal; head to foot
   Now is he total gules; horridly trick'd
   With blood of fathers, mothers, daughters, sons,   455
   Baked and impasted with the parching streets,
   That lend a tyrannous and damned light
   To their lord's murder: roasted in wrath and fire,
   And thus o'er-sized with coagulate gore,
   With eyes like carbuncles, the hellish Pyrrhus   460
   Old grandsire Priam seeks.

   So, proceed you.
Polonius: 'Fore God, my lord, well spoken; with good accent
   and good discretion.
First Player: Anon he finds him   465

470   *fell:* cruel

471-473   *Then senseless . . . base:* As Priam falls, the city crashes down; *Ilium:* Troy

474   *Takes prisoner Pyrrhus' ear:* Pyrrhus is transfixed by the sound.

477   *painted:* motionless, as in a painting

478   *neutral:* indifferent or undecided person

480   *against:* before

481   *rack:* storm clouds

482   *orb:* the earth

486   *Cyclops:* in Roman mythology, a race of one-eyed giants who worked for Vulcan, the gods' blacksmith

487   *Mars:* Roman god of war; *for proof eterne:* forever able to withstand blows

491   *synod:* assembly

492   *fellies:* pieces of wood forming the rim of a wheel

493   *round nave:* hub

497   *Hecuba:* wife of Priam

501   *mobled:* muffled

Striking too short at Greeks; his antique sword,
Rebellious to his arm, lies where it falls,
Repugnant to command: unequal match'd,
Pyrrhus at Priam drives; in rage strikes wide;
But with the whiff and wind of his fell sword   470
The unnerved father falls. Then senseless Ilium,
Seeming to feel his blow, with flaming top
Stoops to his base, and with a hideous crash
Takes prisoner Pyrrhus' ear: for, lo! his sword,
Which was declining on the milky head   475
Of reverend Priam, seem'd i' the air to stick:
So, as a painted tyrant, Pyrrhus stood,
And like a neutral to his will and matter,
Did nothing.
But, as we often see, against some storm,   480
A silence in the heavens, the rack stand still,
The bold winds speechless and the orb below
As hush as death, anon the dreadful thunder
Doth rend the region, so after Pyrrhus' pause
Aroused vengeance sets him new awork;   485
And never did the Cyclops' hammers fall
On Mars's armours, forged for proof eterne,
With less remorse than Pyrrhus' bleeding sword
Now falls on Priam.—
Out, out, thou strumpet, Fortune! All you gods,   490
In general synod, take away her power,
Break all the spokes and fellies from her wheel,
And bowl the round nave down the hill of heaven
As low as to the fiends.

Polonius: This is too long.
Hamlet: It shall to the barber's, with your beard.   495
   Prithee, say on. He's for a jig or a tale of bawdry, or he
   sleeps. Say on; come to Hecuba.

First Player: But who, O, who hath seen the mobled
      queen,—
Hamlet: "The mobled queen"?   500
Polonius: That's good: "mobled queen" is good.
First Player: Run barefoot up and down, threat'ning the
      flames

503   *bisson rheum:* blinding tears

505   *o'erteemed:* worn out with childbearing

514-515 *Would have . . . gods:* would have made the blazing stars
         weep and roused compassion in the gods; *milch:* moist

516   *turned his colour:* turned pale

521   *abstracts and brief chronicles:* summaries and short
         histories

525   *Od's bodykins:* God's body

With bisson rheum; a clout about that head
Where late the diadem stood; and for a robe,
About her lank and all o'erteemed loins   505
A blanket, in the alarm of fear caught up;
Who this had seen, with tongue in venom steep'd
'Gainst Fortune's state would treason have pronounced:
But if the gods themselves did see her then,
When she saw Pyrrhus make malicious sport   510
In mincing with his sword her husband's limbs,
The instant burst of clamour that she made,
Unless things mortal move them not at all,
Would have made milch the burning eyes of heaven
And passion in the gods.   515

Polonius: Look, whether he has not turned his colour and
     has tears in's eyes. Pray you, no more.
Hamlet: 'Tis well; I'll have thee speak out the rest of this
     soon. Good my lord, will you see the players well
     bestowed? Do you hear, let them be well used, for they   520
     are the abstracts and brief chronicles of the time: after
     your death you were better have a bad epitaph than
     their ill report while you live.
Polonius: My lord, I will use them according to their desert.
Hamlet: Od's bodykins, man, better: use every man after   525
     his desert, and who should 'scape whipping! Use them
     after your own honour and dignity: the less they
     deserve, the more merit is in your bounty. Take them
     in.
Polonius: Come, sirs.   530
Hamlet: Follow him, friends: we'll hear a play tomorrow.
     [*Exit Polonius, with all the Players but the First.*] Dost
     thou hear me, old friend; can you play the Murder
     of Gonzago?
First Player: Ay, my lord.   535
Hamlet: We'll have't to-morrow night. You could, for a need,
     study a speech of some dozen or sixteen lines, which
     I would set down, and insert in't, could you not?
First Player: Ay, my lord.
Hamlet: Very well. Follow that lord; and look you mock   540
     him not. [*Exit First Player.*] My good friends, I'll leave

545	*rogue:* here, an idle vagrant
547	*dream of passion:* imaginary feeling
548	*conceit:* something conceived in the mind (not real)
549	*her working:* i.e., his soul's working; *all his visage wann'd:* his face became pale
550	*distraction in's aspect:* his appearance full of agitation
551-552	*his whole function . . . conceit:* all his actions suiting his interpretation
559	*appal the free:* frighten innocent people
560	*Confound:* confuse; *amaze:* bewilder
563	*muddy-mettled:* dull-spirited; *peak:* mope
564	*John-a-dreams:* a dull, dreamy person; *unpregnant of my cause:* without plans for revenge
566	*property:* possessions; here, the crown and his wife
567	*defeat:* destruction, ruin
568-570	Hamlet is citing actions which should provoke a strong response.
573	*'Swounds:* God's wounds (a mild oath).
574	*pigeon-liver'd:* The liver was considered the source of courage. It was thought pigeons were mild-mannered because they had no gall, a fluid secreted by the liver.
576	*kites:* birds of prey, similar to hawks
577	*offal:* guts
578	*kindless:* unnatural

you till night: you are welcome to Elsinore.
Rosencrantz: Good my lord!
Hamlet: Ay, so, God be wi' you!
                        [*Exeunt Rosencrantz and Guildenstern.*]
                            Now I am alone.
O, what a rogue and peasant slave am I!   545
Is it not monstrous that this player here,
But in a fiction, in a dream of passion,
Could force his soul so to his whole conceit
That from her working all his visage wann'd;
Tears in his eyes, distraction in's aspect,   550
A broken voice, and his whole function suiting
With forms to his conceit? And all for nothing!
For Hecuba!
What's Hecuba to him, or he to Hecuba
That he should weep for her? What would he do,   555
Had he the motive and the cue for passion
That I have? He would drown the stage with tears
And cleave the general ear with horrid speech,
Make mad the guilty and appal the free,
Confound the ignorant, and amaze indeed   560
The very faculties of eyes and ears.
Yet I,
A dull and muddy-mettled rascal, peak,
Like John-a-dreams, unpregnant of my cause,
And can say nothing; no, not for a king,   565
Upon whose property and most dear life
A damn'd defeat was made. Am I a coward?
Who calls me villain? breaks my pate across?
Plucks off my beard, and blows it in my face?
Tweaks me by the nose? gives me the lie i' the throat,   570
As deep as to the lungs? Who does me this?
Ha!
'Swounds, I should take it: for it cannot be
But I am pigeon-liver'd, and lack gall
To make oppression bitter, or ere this   575
I should have fatted all the region kites
With this slave's offal. Bloody, bawdy villain!
Remorseless, treacherous, lecherous, kindless villain!
O vengeance!—

585   *scullion:* the lowest of the servants, the person who washed the dishes

586   *About, my brain!:* Get to your work, brains!

590   *malefactions:* evil deeds

595   *tent him to the quick:* probe him deeply; *blench:* flinch

596-598   In Shakespeare's time, people believed that ghosts who claimed to be the spirit of a particular person were sometimes the Devil in disguise.

599   *melancholy:* The word "melancholy" denoted two different conditions. Sometimes it meant temporary depression or low spirits. It could also mean a well-recognized disease believed to be caused by an imbalance of "humours" in the body.

601   *abuses:* deceives

602   *relative:* relevant

Why, what an ass am I! This is most brave,   580
That I, the son of the dear murder'd,
Prompted to my revenge by heaven and hell,
Must, like a whore, unpack my heart with words,
And fall a cursing, like a very drab,
A scullion!   585
Fie upon't! foh! About, my brain! Hum, I have heard,
That guilty creatures, sitting at a play,
Have by the very cunning of the scene
Been struck so to the soul that presently
They have proclaim'd their malefactions;   590
For murder, though it hath no tongue, will speak
With most miraculous organ. I'll have these players
Play something like the murder of my father
Before mine uncle: I'll observe his looks;
I'll tent him to the quick; if he but blench,   595
I know my course. The spirit that I have seen
May be the devil: and the devil hath power
To assume a pleasing shape; yea, and, perhaps
Out of my weakness and my melancholy,
As he is very potent with such spirits,   600
Abuses me to damn me. I'll have grounds
More relative than this. The play's the thing
Wherein I'll catch the conscience of the king.

                                                    [*Exit.*]

Act 2, Scene 2: Activities

1. Suppose that you were one of the attendants present in the room during the first part of this scene (up to line 168). Write an anonymous note to Hamlet warning him about the strategy of the King and Polonius. Your letter should include enough information to convince Hamlet that you are a reliable source. Read the letter to your group.

2. Rumours of Hamlet's "madness" have leaked out of the castle. You are a writer for a tabloid newspaper. You have been assigned to conduct a series of interviews to follow up on these rumours. Make a list of the characters you would interview and the questions you would ask each one. Plan your questions carefully so that the responses would be revealing. Then write the headline for your article.

3. In your group, choose a few of Hamlet's replies to Polonius in their conversation (lines 169–217). Do you think that Hamlet has convinced Polonius that he is insane? Report your opinions to the class, giving your reasons.

4. As a class, read Hamlet's description to Rosencrantz and Guildenstern of how his view of life has changed (lines 293–310). In your group, select a few of the images he uses in this speech that appeal to you. Using newspapers, magazines, or the Internet, find visual images that represent these word images for you. Create a display of these visual images in your classroom.

5. What are your first impressions of Rosencrantz and Guildenstern? Explain why you would or would not want them as friends.

6. As a class, read lines 545–585 in Hamlet's soliloquy at the end of this scene. Discuss why Hamlet is so angry at himself. Do you think that his anger is justified?

7. Hamlet says that watching a play can cause guilty people to confess their crimes (lines 586–596). In your group, discuss whether this could happen nowadays. In your journal, make a note of any plays, movies, or television programs that have influenced you to change something in your own life. Explain why you think they had such a strong impact on you.

Act 2: Consider the Whole Act

1. Prepare a front page of a newspaper or an electronic newsletter about the rumours that have leaked out of the castle concerning Hamlet's madness. You will need to attract readers by emphasizing the sensationalistic aspects of Hamlet's change and hinting at reasons. Your readers will also want to know how others have been affected. Share your front page with the class either by posting a mock-up of the newspaper on the bulletin board or by transmitting it electronically.

2. Using sources such as the Internet, an encyclopedia, or a library, research Revenge Tragedy, which was a popular form of theatre in Shakespeare's time. In what ways is *Hamlet* as a play similar to or different from such tragedies? Write an outline of the similarities and differences, and share your notes with the class.

3. Polonius says that wise people "By indirections find directions out" (II, i, 66). Find as many examples as you can in this Act of people achieving their purposes indirectly or by pretending. What atmosphere does this theme add to the play? Write a short essay on this topic and present it to the class.

For the next scene . . .

Suppose that you have a friend like Hamlet, who thinks deeply and reacts sensitively to events around him or her. Recently your friend has said, "What's the purpose of life, if there are more problems and sorrow than joy and hope?" In your journal, formulate a response to your friend, to prepare yourself for your next conversation.

Act 3, Scene 1

In this scene . . .

Rosencrantz and Guildenstern report to the King that they have not found the cause of Hamlet's strange behaviour. Polonius and Claudius go ahead with their plan to eavesdrop on Hamlet's conversation with Ophelia. When Polonius makes a comment about hypocrisy, this troubles Claudius and prompts him to reveal his guilty conscience in an aside to the audience. Hamlet enters alone, thinking aloud once again about the human condition. Then he catches sight of Ophelia praying. When Ophelia tries to return some love tokens Hamlet gave her earlier, Hamlet replies by insulting Ophelia and women in general. Claudius is not convinced by what he has overheard that Hamlet is mad, but he claims that Hamlet is dangerous. He announces his plan to send Hamlet on a mission to England. Polonius still insists that Hamlet's behaviour is caused by lovesickness, and suggests eavesdropping on a conversation between Hamlet and his mother.

1   *drift of circumstance:* roundabout conversations

2   *puts on this confusion:* pretends to be mad in this way

7   *forward to be sounded:* open to questioning

12   *with much . . . disposition:* behaving artificially

13   *Niggard of question:* hardly speaking (Notice the distortion in Rosencrantz and Guildenstern's report to the King.)

14   *assay him:* get him involved in

17   *o'er-raught:* overtook

22   *beseech'd:* asked

26   *give him a further edge:* encourage him

Act 3, Scene 1

A room in the castle.
Enter King, Queen, Polonius,
Ophelia, Rosencrantz, and
Guildenstern.

King: And can you, by no drift of circumstance,
   Get from him why he puts on this confusion,
   Grating so harshly all his days of quiet
   With turbulent and dangerous lunacy?
Rosencrantz: He does confess he feels himself distracted,   5
   But from what cause he will by no means speak.
Guildenstern: Nor do we find him forward to be sounded;
   But, with a crafty madness, keeps aloof,
   When we would bring him on to some confession
   Of his true state.
Queen: Did he receive you well?   10
Rosencrantz: Most like a gentleman.
Guildenstern: But with much forcing of his disposition.
Rosencrantz: Niggard of question, but, of our demands,
   Most free in his reply.
Queen: Did you assay him
   To any pastime?   15
Rosencrantz: Madam, it so fell out that certain players
   We o'er-raught on the way: of these we told him,
   And there did seem in him a kind of joy
   To hear of it: they are about the court,
   And, as I think, they have already order   20
   This night to play before him.
Polonius: 'Tis most true:
   And he beseech'd me to entreat your majesties
   To hear and see the matter.
King: With all my heart; and it doth much content me
   To hear him so inclined.   25
   Good gentlemen, give him a further edge,
   And drive his purpose on to these delights.

29	*closely:* secretly

31	*Affront:* come face to face with
32	*espials:* spies
33	*bestow:* place (in this case, hide)

41	*wonted way:* accustomed behaviour

44	*this book:* probably a book of prayers
45-46	*That show . . . loneliness:* so that your being at prayer will explain why you are here alone
47-49	*with devotion's visage . . . himself:* with a display of virtuous behaviour we conceal our wickedness

51	*smart:* sharp, stinging. The image is of a wrongdoer being whipped so that he will repent.
52-54	*The harlot's . . . word:* The prostitute's makeup is just as ugly as the cheek it covers. In the same way, my hypocritical behaviour is just as ugly as the deed it is covering up.
52	*plastering art:* skill in applying makeup

57	*To be, or not to be:* The general consensus among Shakespeare scholars is that Hamlet is contemplating suicide. What other interpretations are possible?

Rosencrantz: We shall, my lord.
                    [*Exeunt Rosencrantz and Guildenstern.*]
King: Sweet Gertrude, leave us too:
　For we have closely sent for Hamlet hither,
　That he, as 'twere by accident, may here   30
　Affront Ophelia.
　Her father and myself, lawful espials,
　Will so bestow ourselves that, seeing unseen,
　We may of their encounter frankly judge,
　And gather by him, as he is behaved,   35
　If't be the affliction of his love or no
　That thus he suffers for.
Queen: I shall obey you:
　And for your part, Ophelia, I do wish
　That your good beauties be the happy cause
　Of Hamlet's wildness: so shall I hope your virtues   40
　Will bring him to his wonted way again,
　To both your honours.
Ophelia: Madam, I wish it may.
                                        [*Exit Queen.*]
Polonius: Ophelia, walk you here. Gracious, so please you,
　We will bestow ourselves. [*To Ophelia.*] Read on this
　　book;
　That show of such an exercise may colour   45
　Your loneliness. We are oft to blame in this,—
　'Tis too much proved that, with devotion's visage,
　And pious action, we do sugar o'er
　The devil himself.
King [*Aside*]: O, 'tis too true!   50
　How smart a lash that speech doth give my conscience!
　The harlot's cheek, beautied with plastering art,
　Is not more ugly to the thing that helps it
　Than is my deed to my most painted word:
　O heavy burden!   55
Polonius: I hear him coming; let's withdraw, my lord.
                              [*Exeunt King and Polonius.*]

　[*Enter Hamlet.*]

Hamlet: To be, or not to be: that is the question:
　Whether 'tis nobler in the mind to suffer

59	*The slings . . . fortune:* Fortune is described as waging war on humans.
61	*opposing:* struggling, fighting back
62	*No more:* merely this
64	*That flesh is heir to:* that are part of our human condition; *consummation:* final ending
66	*rub:* obstacle
68	*shuffled off . . . coil:* gotten rid of this life of turmoil
69-70	*there's the respect . . . life:* there's the consideration that causes us to live through a long life filled with calamity
71	*the whips and scorns of time:* the harsh experiences of life
72	*contumely:* scorn, insults
74-75	*of office:* of people in official positions; *the spurns . . . takes:* the insults that inferior people direct at quiet, worthy people
76	*quietus:* release
77	*bodkin:* dagger; *fardels:* burdens
80	*bourn:* limit, boundary
84	*conscience:* thinking
85	*the native hue of resolution:* the natural colour of courage
87	*pith and moment:* significance
88	*their currents turn awry:* The image is of a river that loses its force when its path is changed.
90-91	*Nymph . . . remember'd:* Lady, ask forgiveness for my sins while you are playing.
94	*remembrances:* gifts

The slings and arrows of outrageous fortune,
Or to take arms against a sea of troubles,   60
And by opposing end them. To die: to sleep:
No more; and by a sleep to say we end
The heart-ache, and the thousand natural shocks
That flesh is heir to, 'tis a consummation
Devoutly to be wish'd. To die, to sleep;   65
To sleep: perchance to dream: ay, there's the rub;
For in that sleep of death what dreams may come,
When we have shuffled off this mortal coil,
Must give us pause: there's the respect
That makes calamity of so long life: 70
For who would bear the whips and scorns of time,
The oppressor's wrong, the proud man's contumely,
The pang of despised love, the law's delay,
The insolence of office, and the spurns
That patient merit of the unworthy takes,   75
When he himself might his quietus make
With a bare bodkin? who would fardels bear,
To grunt and sweat under a weary life,
But that the dread of something after death,
The undiscover'd country from whose bourn   80
No traveller returns, puzzles the will,
And makes us rather bear those ills we have
Than fly to others that we know not of?
Thus conscience does make cowards of us all,
And thus the native hue of resolution   85
Is sicklied o'er with the pale cast of thought,
And enterprises of great pith and moment
With this regard their currents turn awry
And lose the name of action. Soft you now!
The fair Ophelia! Nymph, in thy orisons   90
Be all my sins remember'd.
Ophelia: Good my lord,
How does your honour for this many a day?
Hamlet: I humbly thank you: well, well, well.
Ophelia: My lord, I have remembrances of yours,
That I have longed long to re-deliver;   95
I pray you, now receive them.
Hamlet: No, not I. I never gave you aught.

100	*their perfume lost:* since they have lost the value that your affection once gave them
102	*wax:* become
104	*honest:* truthful or virtuous
108-109	*your honesty . . . beauty:* Your chastity ("honesty") should prevent contact with your beauty.
110	*commerce:* association
111-113	*for the power . . . likeness:* Beauty will corrupt chastity more readily than chastity will purify beauty.
117-118	*for virtue . . . relish of it:* A new branch cannot be grafted onto an ailing tree without also being infected. In the same way, virtue cannot take hold in human nature without being tainted by sinfulness.
118	*inoculate:* graft; *old stock:* original tree (here, a reference to the original sin of Adam); *relish of it:* taste of it (i.e., retain traces of it)
121	*nunnery:* convent; a place where Ophelia will be free of sin and temptation. The word also means "brothel."
122	*indifferent:* more or less, moderately
128	*crawling:* The image is of a worm.
129	*arrant knaves:* extreme rascals

Ophelia: My honour'd lord, I know right well you did;
   And with them words of so sweet breath composed
   As made the things more rich: their perfume lost,   100
   Take these again; for to the noble mind
   Rich gifts wax poor when givers prove unkind.
   There, my lord.
Hamlet: Ha, ha! are you honest?
Ophelia: My lord?   105
Hamlet: Are you fair?
Ophelia: What means your lordship?
Hamlet: That if you be honest and fair, your honesty should
   admit no discourse to your beauty.
Ophelia: Could beauty, my lord, have better commerce than
   with honesty?   110
Hamlet: Ay, truly; for the power of beauty will sooner
   transform honesty from what it is to a bawd than the
   force of honesty can translate beauty into his likeness:
   this was sometime a paradox, but now the time gives
   it proof. I did love you once.   115
Ophelia: Indeed, my lord, you made me believe so.
Hamlet: You should not have believed me: for virtue cannot
   so inoculate our old stock but we shall relish of it: I
   loved you not.
Ophelia: I was the more deceived.   120
Hamlet: Get thee to a nunnery: why wouldst thou be a
   breeder of sinners? I am myself indifferent honest, but
   yet I could accuse me of such things that it were better
   my mother had not borne me: I am very proud,
   revengeful, ambitious, with more offences at my beck   125
   than I have thoughts to put them in, imagination to
   give them shape, or time to act them in. What should
   such fellows as I do crawling between heaven and
   earth! We are arrant knaves, all; believe none of us. Go
   thy ways to a nunnery. Where's your father?   130
Ophelia: At home, my lord.
Hamlet: Let the doors be shut upon him, that he may play
   the fool nowhere but in's own house. Farewell.
Ophelia: O, help him, you sweet heavens!
Hamlet: If thou dost marry, I'll give thee this plague for   135
   thy dowry: be thou as chaste as ice, as pure as snow,

137	*calumny:* slander
143	*paintings:* women's makeup
145	*you jig, you amble:* These are dancing movements that suggest sexual, seductive behaviour; *lisp:* In Shakespeare's time, lisping was associated with sexually immoral behaviour.
146	*nickname God's creatures:* give offensive, immodest nicknames to things
146-147	*make your . . . ignorance:* excuse your bad behaviour by saying you didn't know any better
153-156	Ophelia is describing Hamlet as the ideal Renaissance man.
154	*expectancy:* hope. This may refer also to the expectation that Hamlet will inherit the throne; *rose:* symbol of perfection
155	*The glass . . . form:* the ideal of fashion and behaviour; *glass:* mirror; *mould:* model
158	*suck'd the honey of his music vows:* believed his sweet words
161	*blown youth:* youth in his prime (in full bloom)
162	*Blasted with ecstasy:* destroyed by madness
164	*affections:* feelings
168	*doubt:* suspect
172	*our neglected tribute:* payments owing to Denmark
173	*Haply:* perhaps
174	*variable objects:* change of environment

thou shalt not escape calumny. Get thee to a nunnery,
go; farewell. Or, if thou wilt needs marry, marry a
fool; for wise men know well enough what monsters you
make of them. To a nunnery, go; and quickly too.   140
Farewell.
Ophelia: O heavenly powers, restore him!
Hamlet: I have heard of your paintings too, well enough.
    God hath given you one face, and you make
    yourselves another; you jig, you amble, and you lisp,   145
    and nickname God's creatures, and make your
    wantonness your ignorance. Go to, I'll no more on't;
    it hath made me mad. I say, we will have no more
    marriages: those that are married already, all but
    one, shall live; the rest shall keep as they are. To a   150
    nunnery, go.   [*Exit Hamlet.*]
Ophelia: O, what a noble mind is here o'erthrown!
    The courtier's, soldier's, scholar's, eye, tongue, sword;
    The expectancy and rose of the fair state,
    The glass of fashion and the mould of form,   155
    The observed of all observers, quite, quite down!
    And I, of ladies most deject and wretched,
    That suck'd the honey of his music vows,
    Now see that noble and most sovereign reason,
    Like sweet bells jangled, out of tune and harsh;   160
    That unmatch'd form and feature of blown youth
    Blasted with ecstasy: O, woe is me,
    To have seen what I have seen, see what I see!

    [*Re-enter King and Polonius.*]

King: Love! his affections do not that way tend;
    Nor what he spake, though it lack'd form a little,   165
    Was not like madness. There's something in his soul
    O'er which his melancholy sits on brood,
    And I do doubt the hatch and the disclose
    Will be some danger: which for to prevent,
    I have in quick determination   170
    Thus set it down: he shall with speed to England
    For the demand of our neglected tribute:
    Haply, the seas, and countries different
    With variable objects shall expel

177   *fashion of himself:* his normal behaviour

185   *grief:* grievances; *round:* straightforward

186-187   *I'll be placed . . . conference:* I'll be hidden where I can hear everything; *find him not:* doesn't find out the truth

This something-settled matter in his heart,   175
Whereon his brains still beating puts him thus
From fashion of himself. What think you on't?
Polonius: It shall do well; but yet do I believe
The origin and commencement of his grief
Sprung from neglected love. How now, Ophelia!   180
You need not tell us what Lord Hamlet said;
We heard it all. My lord, do as you please;
But, if you hold it fit, after the play,
Let his queen mother all alone entreat him
To show his grief; let her be round with him;   185
And I'll be placed, so please you, in the ear
Of all their conference. If she find him not,
To England send him, or confine him where
Your wisdom best shall think.
King: It shall be so;
Madness in great ones must not unwatch'd go.   190
                                      [Exeunt.]

Act 3, Scene 1: Activities

1. In the role of Ophelia, write a diary entry reacting to your encounter with Hamlet. Include your current feelings and your reflections on how Hamlet has changed.

2. Claudius admits that he is suffering from a guilty conscience (lines 50–55). Does this confession change your opinion of him in some way? Explain your answer.

3. In his soliloquy (lines 57–89), Hamlet ranges beyond his own particular situation to contemplate the problems of life in general. If Hamlet were living in modern times, which of the problems listed in the soliloquy might he still include as belonging to our "sea of troubles"? Which of these problems appear regularly in daily newspapers or newscasts?

4. You are the director of a new production of *Hamlet*. The editor of a drama magazine will be interviewing you about your ideas for the nunnery scene. The interviewer has sent you the questions beforehand. Prepare answers for the interview by addressing each of these questions:

   • When and how will Hamlet discover that Claudius and Polonius are spying on him and Ophelia?

   • In your interpretation of "Get thee to a nunnery," is a nunnery a convent or a brothel? How will you convey this to a modern audience?

   • After Hamlet's exit (line 151), would you consider having Hamlet rush back to kiss Ophelia, or make some other gesture revealing his emotions, as has been done in some other productions?

   Add two or three of your own questions. Then conduct the interviews in pairs for the class.

5. In your group, create a choral reading of the "To be, or not to be" soliloquy. In order to do this, first break the soliloquy up into shorter passages. Then decide how to read each passage. You should consider the following:

    - Is the passage to be read as a solo, a duet, an ensemble, or as a single voice against a group background?

    - Can you make use of alternating voices, repetition, or echoes?

    - How loudly or softly should the passage be read?

    - What tone of voice should you use?

    - How quickly should you read? What rhythm is appropriate?

    - What words or phrases should be emphasized?

    Once you have decided how each passage will be read and have assigned all the parts, practise your reading a few times. Work out the best physical arrangement for the speakers. (You may also decide that you need one person to act as a conductor.) Perform your reading for the class.

For the next scene . . .

In your journal, write about an incident when you trapped someone (or when someone trapped you) into admitting guilt about something. How did you feel?

Act 3, Scene 2

In this scene . . .

Hamlet gives the actors some last-minute advice on how to perform the play. He then confides in Horatio, telling him of his plan to test Claudius' guilt. Horatio promises to observe Claudius' reaction to the play. When the King and Queen, Polonius, Ophelia, and the rest of the court enter, Hamlet again plays the madman. The performance of *The Mousetrap* begins with a "dumb show" or pantomime of the plot. Then the play itself gets underway. At the moment when the murder of the King is enacted, Claudius walks out, putting an end to the performance. Hamlet and Horatio are both convinced of Claudius' guilt. As the scene ends, Rosencrantz and Guildenstern return to tell Hamlet that the King is angry. Polonius informs Hamlet that his mother wishes to speak to him.

1-47	Hamlet, in his instructions to the actors, is probably reflecting Shakespeare's own preferences for a natural, unexaggerated, sincere style of acting.
2	*trippingly on the tongue:* smoothly; *mouth:* say the words without showing you understand them
4	*saw the air:* use exaggerated hand gestures
7	*temperance:* self-control
9	*robustious:* violent, blustering; *periwig-pated:* wearing a wig
9-10	*tear a passion . . . rags:* use a melodramatic, exaggerated acting style
11	*groundlings:* rowdy spectators standing in the pit (i.e., in the innyard or the ground floor of the theatre)
11-12	*are capable . . . noise:* enjoy only the lowest form of entertainment (pantomime)
13,14	*Termagant, Herod:* violent, ranting stage characters
16-24	In these lines, Hamlet is reflecting the Renaissance idea that drama should present an image of real life.
19	*modesty:* moderation
20	*from:* far from
23	*scorn:* that which should be scorned
24	*pressure:* image
25	*come tardy off:* done inadequately
27	*censure:* judgment; *in your allowance:* in your opinion

Scene 2

A hall in the same.
Enter Hamlet and Players.

Hamlet: Speak the speech, I pray you, as I pronounced it
    to you, trippingly on the tongue: but if you mouth it,
    as many of your players do, I had as lief the town-
    crier spoke my lines. Nor do not saw the air too much
    with your hand, thus: but use all gently: for in the   5
    very torrent, tempest, and, as I may say, whirlwind of
    your passion, you must acquire and beget a temperance
    that may give it smoothness. O, it offends me to the
    soul, to see a robustious periwig-pated fellow tear a
    passion to tatters, to very rags, to split the ears of the   10
    groundlings, who, for the most part, are capable of
    nothing but inexplicable dumb shows and noise: I could
    have such a fellow whipped for o'erdoing Termagant;
    it out-herods Herod: pray you, avoid it.
First Player: I warrant your honour.   15
Hamlet: Be not too tame neither, but let your own discretion
    be your tutor: suit the action to the word, the word
    to the action; with this special observance, that you
    o'erstep not the modesty of nature; for anything so
    overdone is from the purpose of playing, whose end,   20
    both at the first and now, was and is, to hold, as 'twere,
    the mirror up to nature; to show virtue her own
    feature, scorn her own image, and the very age and
    body of the time his form and pressure. Now this
    overdone or come tardy off, though it make the   25
    unskilful laugh, cannot but make the judicious grieve;
    the censure of the which one must in your allowance
    o'erweigh a whole theatre of others. O, there be
    players that I have seen play, and heard others praise,
    and that highly, not to speak it profanely, that neither   30

33   *journeymen:* unskilled workers, craftsmen who have not yet mastered their trade

36   *indifferently:* more or less

38-45   This is a criticism of comedians who ad lib among themselves on stage, drawing attention away from the main action.

41   *barren:* brainless

47   *presently:* immediately

53   *just:* well-balanced

54   *as e'er . . . coped withal:* as I have ever encountered

59   *let . . . pomp:* Let the flatterer use sugary words on those rich men who make a ridiculous display of their wealth

60-61   *And crook . . . fawning:* kneel and fawn in order to gain some advantage (thrift); *pregnant:* ever-ready

having the accent of Christians, nor the gait of Christian,
pagan, nor man, have so strutted and bellowed, that
I have thought some of nature's journeymen had made
men, and not made them well, they imitated humanity
so abominably.   35
First Player: I hope we have reformed that indifferently with
us, sir.
Hamlet: O, reform it altogether. And let those that play
your clowns speak no more than is set down for them:
for there be of them, that will themselves laugh, to   40
set on some quantity of barren spectators to laugh too,
though in the meantime some necessary question of
the play be then to be considered: that's villainous, and
shows a most pitiful ambition in the fool that uses
it. Go, make you ready.   45

                                            [*Exeunt Players.*]

[*Enter Polonius, Rosencrantz, and Guildenstern.*]

How now, my lord? will the king hear this piece of work?
Polonius: And the queen too, and that presently.
Hamlet: Bid the players make haste.   [*Exit Polonius.*]
   Will you too help to hasten them?
Both: We will, my lord.   50
                         [*Exeunt Rosencrantz and Guildenstern.*]
Hamlet: What ho, Horatio!

[*Enter Horatio.*]

Horatio: Here, sweet lord, at your service.
Hamlet: Horatio, thou art e'en as just a man
   As e'er my conversation coped withal.
Horatio: O, my dear lord,—
Hamlet: Nay, do not think I flatter: 55
   For what advancement may I hope from thee,
   That no revenue hast but thy good spirits,
   To feed and clothe thee? Why should the poor be flatter'd?
   No, let the candied tongue lick absurd pomp,
   And crook the pregnant hinges of the knee   60
   Where thrift may follow fawning. Dost thou hear?
   Since my dear soul was mistress of her choice,

63	*election:* choice
64-67	*thou hast been . . . thanks:* You have accepted both good and bad fortune with a calm disposition.
68	*blood:* Blood represents passion. Hence, "blood" and "judgment" (reason) are opposites, which in Horatio are "well commingled" (well mixed).
78	*with . . . soul:* with your very sharpest observation
79	*occulted:* secret
80	*unkennel:* reveal
81	*damned ghost:* an evil, deceiving ghost
83	*Vulcan's stithy:* the smithy of Vulcan, god of blacksmiths. The image also suggests Hell.
86	*In censure of his seeming:* in judging his appearance
89	*idle:* unoccupied or possibly mad
91	*fares:* Claudius probably means "How are (fare) you, Hamlet?" Hamlet purposely misinterprets the question as "What do you eat?"
92	*chameleon:* According to an ancient belief, the chameleon feeds on air.
94-95	*I have . . . mine:* These words mean nothing to me.

And could of men distinguish, her election
Hath seal'd thee for herself: for thou has been
As one, in suffering all, that suffers nothing;   65
A man that fortune's buffets and rewards
Hast ta'en with equal thanks: and blessed are those
Whose blood and judgment are so well commingled
That they are not a pipe for Fortune's finger
To sound what stop she please. Give me that man   70
That is not passion's slave, and I will wear him
In my heart's core, ay, in my heart of heart,
As I do thee. Something too much of this.
There is a play to-night before the king;
One scene of it comes near the circumstance   75
Which I have told thee of my father's death:
I prithee, when thou seest that act a-foot,
Even with the very comment of thy soul
Observe mine uncle: if his occulted guilt
Do not itself unkennel in one speech,   80
It is a damned ghost that we have seen,
And my imaginations are as foul
As Vulcan's stithy. Give him heedful note;
For I mine eyes will rivet to his face,
And after we will both our judgments join   85
In censure of his seeming.
Horatio: Well, my lord:
If he steal aught the whilst this play is playing,
And 'scape detecting, I will pay the theft.
Hamlet: They are coming to the play; I must be idle:
Get you a place.   90

[*Danish march. A flourish. Enter King, Queen, Polonius,
Ophelia, Rosencrantz, Guildenstern, and other Lords
attendant with the Guard, carrying torches.*]

King: How fares our cousin Hamlet?
Hamlet: Excellent, i' faith; of the chameleon's dish: I eat
the air, promise-crammed; you cannot feed capons so.
King: I have nothing with this answer, Hamlet; these words
are not mine.   95
Hamlet: No, nor mine now. [*To Polonius.*] My lord, you
played once in the university, you say?

107   *here's metal more attractive:* Ophelia (metal) has more magnetic (attractive) power.

109   *Lady . . . lap?:* Hamlet implies something indecent and then, in line 113, denies it.

113   *country matters:* boorish, indecent behaviour

121   *your only jig-maker:* chief comedian

127   *a suit of sables:* rich furs (not necessarily black)

130-131   *shall he . . . on:* he will be forgotten; *hobby-horse:* In earlier times, the hobby-horse (a man dressed in a horse costume) had been part of the May Day celebrations. The Puritans, however, had suppressed the May Day rituals. Hence, the hobby-horse was forgotten.

Stage directions

(following line 133): *Hautboys:* renaissance wind instrument, the forerunner of the modern oboe; *the dumb show:* this is a pantomime preview of the action of the play that will follow. There are many differing opinions among critics as to whether or not Claudius sees the dumb show, since he seems not to react to it.

Polonius: That I did, my lord, and was accounted a good
    actor.
Hamlet: What did you enact? 100
Polonius: I did enact Julius Cæsar: I was killed i' the Capitol:
    Brutus killed me.
Hamlet: It was a brute part of him to kill so capital a calf
    there. Be the players ready?
Rosencrantz: Ay, my lord; they stay upon your patience. 105
Queen: Come hither, my dear Hamlet, sit by me.
Hamlet: No, good mother, here's metal more attractive.
Polonius: O ho! do you mark that?   [*To the King.*]
Hamlet: Lady, shall I lie in your lap?
                      [*Lying down at Ophelia's feet.*]
Ophelia: No, my lord. 110
Hamlet: I mean, my head upon your lap?
Ophelia: Ay, my lord.
Hamlet: Do you think I meant country matters?
Ophelia: I think nothing, my lord.
Hamlet: That's a fair thought to lie between maids' legs. 115
Ophelia: What is, my lord?
Hamlet: Nothing!
Ophelia: You are merry, my lord.
Hamlet: Who, I?
Ophelia: Ay, my lord. 120
Hamlet: O God, your only jig-maker. What should a man
    do, but be merry? for, look you, how cheerfully my
    mother looks, and my father died within these two
    hours.
Ophelia: Nay, 'tis twice two months, my lord. 125
Hamlet: So long? Nay, then, let the devil wear black, for
    I'll have a suit of sables. O heavens! die two months
    ago, and not forgotten yet? Then there's hope a great
    man's memory may outlive his life half a year: but,
    by'r lady, he must build churches then: or else shall 130
    he suffer not thinking on, with the hobby-horse,
    whose epitaph is, "For, O, for, O, the hobby-horse is
    forgot."

[*Hautboys play. The dumb show enters.*]

[*Enter a King and a Queen, very lovingly; the Queen*

135   *miching mallecho:* sneaking mischief

136   *imports the argument:* presents the theme

138-139   *The players . . . tell all:* Is Hamlet annoyed that the actors have given away too much of the story in the dumb show?

139   *keep counsel:* keep a secret

144   *naught:* naughty

148   *posy of a ring:* a short motto engraved inside a ring

151   *Phoebus' cart:* the chariot of the sun-god, Phoebus Apollo

152   *Neptune's salt wash:* the sea. (Neptune was the Roman god of the sea); *Tellus' orbed ground:* the earth. Tellus mater (mother earth) was the Roman goddess of the earth.

155   *Hymen:* god of marriage

*embracing him and he her. She kneels, and makes show
of protestation unto him. He takes her up, and declines his
head upon her neck; lays him down upon a bank of
flowers; she, seeing him asleep, leaves him. Anon comes in
a fellow, takes off his crown, kisses it, and pours poison
in the King's ears, and exit. The Queen returns; finds the
King dead, and makes passionate action. The Poisoner,
with some two or three Mutes, comes in again, seeming to
lament with her. The dead body is carried away. The
Poisoner woos the Queen with gifts; she seems loath and
unwilling awhile, but, in the end, accepts his love.]*

[Exeunt.]

Ophelia: What means this, my lord?

Hamlet: Marry, this is miching mallecho; it means mischief.   135

Ophelia: Belike this show imports the argument of the
    play.

[Enter Prologue.]

Hamlet: We shall know by this fellow: the players cannot
    keep counsel; they'll tell all.

Ophelia: Will he tell us what this show meant?   140

Hamlet: Ay, or any show that you'll show him. Be not
    ashamed to show; he'll not shame to tell you what it
    means.

Ophelia: You are naught, you are naught. I'll mark the play.

  Prologue: For us, and for our tragedy,   145
       Here stooping to your clemency,
       We beg your hearing patiently.

Hamlet: Is this a prologue, or the posy of a ring?

Ophelia: 'Tis brief, my lord.

Hamlet: As woman's love.   150

[Enter two Players, King and Queen.]

  Player King: Full thirty times hath Phœbus' cart gone
    round
    Neptune's salt wash, and Tellus' orbed ground;
    And thirty dozen moons with borrowed sheen
    About the world have times twelve thirties been;
    Since love our hearts, and Hymen did our hands,   155
    Unite commutual in most sacred bands.

161   *distrust:* worry about

162   *Discomfort:* upset

163-164 *For women's fear . . . extremity:* A woman either does not feel fear and love, or feels both in extreme.

170   *My operant powers . . . do:* I am losing my faculties.

173   *confound the rest:* damn the rest

177   *wormwood:* bitter words

178   *instances:* motives

179   *base respects of thrift:* motives of gain

184-187 *Purpose is but . . . be:* Our strong intentions (like unripe fruit on a tree) weaken with time and, forgotten, fall like ripened fruit from the tree.

188-189 *Most necessary . . . debt:* It is inevitable (necessary) that we don't keep (pay) our promises (debt) to ourselves.

192-193 *The violence . . . destroy:* The very intensity of grief or joy prevents us from acting upon them.

194-195 *Where joy . . . accident:* Emotional people experience extreme mood changes, triggered by small things.

Player Queen: So many journeys may the sun and moon
    Make us again count o'er ere love be done!
    But, woe is me, you are so sick of late,
    So far from cheer, and from your former state,   160
    That I distrust you. Yet, though I distrust,
    Discomfort you, my lord, it nothing must:
    For women's fear and love holds quantity;
    In neither aught, or in extremity.
    Now, what my love is, proof hath made you know,   165
    And as my love is sized, my fear is so.
    Where love is great, the littlest doubts are fear;
    Where little fears grow great, great love grows there.
Player King: 'Faith, I must leave thee, love, and shortly
      too;
    My operant powers their functions leave to do: 170
    And thou shalt live in this fair world behind,
    Honour'd, beloved; and haply one as kind
    For husband shalt thou—
Player Queen: O, confound the rest!
    Such love must needs be treason in my breast:
    In second husband let me be accurst!   175
    None wed the second, but who kill'd the first.

Hamlet [*Aside*]: Wormwood, wormwood.
Player Queen: The instances that second marriage move
    Are base respects of thrift, but none of love.
    A second time I kill my husband dead   180
    When second husband kisses me in bed.
Player King: I do believe you think what now you speak,
    But what we do determine oft we break.
    Purpose is but the slave to memory,
    Of violent birth but poor validity: 185
    Which now, like fruit unripe, sticks on the tree,
    But fall unshaken when they mellow be.
    Most necessary 'tis that we forget
    To pay ourselves what to ourselves is debt:
    What to ourselves in passion we propose,   190
    The passion ending, doth the purpose lose.
    The violence of either grief or joy
    Their own enactures with themselves destroy:
    Where joy most revels, grief doth most lament;

196   *for aye:* static (the same forever)

202   *tend:* depend

205   *seasons:* matures (i.e., turns him into)

207-209 *Our wills . . . our own:* The plans we make for the future are very different from what fortune actually brings.

213   *Sport . . . night!:* May I have no enjoyment during the day nor rest at night.

215   *an anchor's cheer:* a hermit's (anchorite's) existence

216   *Each opposite . . . joy:* each unfortunate experience that changes joy to sorrow

223   *rock:* soothe

224   *twain:* two

226   *protests:* declares her feelings too strongly

228   *argument:* plot

Grief joys, joy grieves, on slender accident. 195
This world is not for aye, nor 'tis not strange,
That even our loves should with our fortunes change,
For 'tis a question left us yet to prove,
Whether love lead fortune, or else fortune love.
The great man down, you mark his favourite flies; 200
The poor advanced makes friends of enemies:
And hitherto doth love on fortune tend:
For who not needs shall never lack a friend,
And who in want a hollow friend doth try
Directly seasons him his enemy. 205
But, orderly to end where I begun,
Our wills and fates do so contrary run,
That our devices still are overthrown,
Our thoughts are ours, their ends none of our own;
So think thou wilt no second husband wed, 210
But die thy thoughts when thy first lord is dead.

Player Queen: Nor earth to me give food nor heaven light!
Sport and repose lock from me day and night!
To desperation turn my trust and hope!
An anchor's cheer in prison be my scope! 215
Each opposite, that blanks the face of joy,
Meet what I would have well and it destroy!
Both here and hence pursue me lasting strife,
If, once a widow, ever I be wife!

Hamlet: If she should break it now! 220

Player King: 'Tis deeply sworn. Sweet, leave me here
    awhile:
My spirits grow dull, and fain I would beguile
The tedious day with sleep.   *[Sleeps.]*

Player Queen: Sleep rock thy brain;
And never come mischance between us twain!
                              [Exit.]

Hamlet: Madam, how like you this play? 225

Queen: The lady protests too much, methinks.

Hamlet: O, but she'll keep her word.

King: Have you heard the argument? Is there no offence
    in't?

Hamlet: No, no, they do but jest, poison in jest; no offence 230
    i' the world.

233   *Marry:* by Mary (a mild oath); *Tropically:* metaphorically

237   *free:* innocent

238   *galled jade:* a horse whose shoulders have been rubbed raw by the saddle; *withers:* ridge between a horse's shoulders

238-239 *let . . . unwrung:* Let the guilty ones flinch; the innocent ones feel nothing

241   *chorus:* A chorus would explain or comment on the play's action.

242   *interpret:* The person who interprets in a puppet show explains the puppet's actions.

244   *keen:* sharp-tongued

245   *It would cost . . . edge:* Hamlet is making a lewd comment.

251   *Confederate season:* suitable time

253   *Hecate's ban:* the curse of Hecate, goddess of witchcraft

254   *dire property:* dread power

262   *false fire:* blank cartridge (i.e., make-believe)

King: What do you call the play?

Hamlet: The Mouse-trap. Marry, how? Tropically. This
play is the image of a murder done in Vienna: Gonzago
is the duke's name; his wife, Baptista: you shall see   235
anon: 'tis a knavish piece of work: but what o' that?
your majesty, and we that have free souls, it touches
us not: let the galled jade wince, our withers are
unwrung.

[Enter Lucianus.]

This is one Lucianus, nephew to the king.   240

Ophelia: You are as good as a chorus, my lord.

Hamlet: I could interpret between you and your love, if I
could see the puppets dallying.

Ophelia: You are keen, my lord, you are keen.

Hamlet: It would cost you a groaning to take off my edge.   245

Ophelia: Still better, and worse.

Hamlet: So you must take your husbands. Begin murderer;
pox, leave thy damnable faces, and begin. Come: the
croaking raven doth bellow for revenge.

Lucianus: Thoughts black, hands apt, drugs fit, and time
agreeing;   250
Confederate season, else no creature seeing;
Thou mixture rank, of midnight weeds collected,
With Hecate's ban thrice blasted, thrice infected,
Thy natural magic and dire property,
On wholesome life usurp immediately.   255
                    [Pours the poison in his ears.]

Hamlet: He poisons him i' the garden for his estate. His
name's Gonzago; the story is extant, and writ in choice
Italian: you shall see anon how the murderer gets the
love of Gonzago's wife.   260

Ophelia: The king rises.

Hamlet: What, frighted with false fire!

Queen: How fares my lord?

Polonius: Give o'er the play.

King: Give me some light. Away!

All: Lights, lights, lights!   265
                    [Exeunt all but Hamlet and Horatio.]

Hamlet: Why, let the stricken deer go weep,

270	*a forest of feathers:* part of an actor's costume
271	*turn Turk with me:* turn against me
271-272	*Provincial roses:* roses from Provence (a region in southern France); *razed shoes:* shoes made of leather that has been cut to form a pattern; *cry:* troupe. The image is of a pack of hounds.
276	*Damon:* a loyal friend in mythology
279	*peacock:* The peacock was a symbol of negative qualities such as vanity, pride, and lechery.
88	*perdy:* a mild oath, from "par Dieu"
294	*distempered:* upset, or drunk. Hamlet deliberately mistakes Guildenstern's meaning.
296	*choler:* anger. According to the theory of humours, a choleric person suffered from an excess of bile.
299	*purgation:* cleansing. Hamlet intends two meanings: to get rid of his bile and to get rid of his guilt.
301	*frame:* order

  The hart ungalled play:
For some must watch, while some must sleep;
  So runs the world away.
Would not this, sir, and a forest of feathers—if the rest 270
of my fortunes turn Turk with me—with two Provincial
roses on my razed shoes, get me a fellowship in a cry
of players, sir?

Horatio: Half a share.

Hamlet: A whole one, I.   275
  For thou dost know, O Damon dear,
   This realm dismantled was
  Of Jove himself; and now reigns here
   A very, very—peacock.

Horatio: You might have rhymed.   280

Hamlet: O good Horatio, I'll take the ghost's word for a
  thousand pound. Didst perceive?

Horatio: Very well, my lord.

Hamlet: Upon the talk of the poisoning?

Horatio: I did very well note him.   285

Hamlet: Ah, ha! Come, some music; come the recorders!
  For if the king like not the comedy,
  Why, then, belike, he likes it not, perdy.

[Re-enter Rosencrantz and Guildenstern.]

  Come, some music.

Guildenstern: Good my lord, vouchsafe me a word with you. 290

Hamlet: Sir, a whole history.

Guildenstern: The king, sir,—

Hamlet: Ay, sir, what of him?

Guildenstern: Is in his retirement marvellous distempered.

Hamlet: With drink, sir?   295

Guildenstern: No, my lord, rather with choler.

Hamlet: Your wisdom should show itself more richer to
  signify this to his doctor; for, for me to put him to his
  purgation would perhaps plunge him into more choler.

Guildenstern: Good my lord, put your discourse into some 300
  frame, and start not so wildly from my affair.

Hamlet: I am tame, sir: pronounce.

Guildenstern: The queen, your mother, in most great affliction
  of spirit hath sent me to you.

309 *pardon:* permission to go

318 *admiration:* astonishment

325 *trade:* business

327 *pickers and stealers:* hands

331 *I lack advancement:* Hamlet knows that Rosencrantz and Guildenstern will report this to Claudius.

334 *"While the grass grows":* (a proverb) While the grass grows, the horse starves.

337-338 *why do you . . . toil?":* Why are you setting up a trap for me? The metaphor is taken from hunting. A hunter would get upwind of the prey so that his scent would frighten the animal into running away and into his trap (toil).

339-340 *O . . . unmannerly:* I'm trying so hard to fulfill my duty (to the King) that I've been rude to you.

Hamlet: You are welcome.   305

Guildenstern: Nay, good my lord, this courtesy is not of the
    right breed. If it shall please you to make me a
    wholesome answer, I will do your mother's
    commandment: if not, your pardon and my return shall
    be the end of my business.   310

Hamlet: Sir, I cannot.

Guildenstern: What, my lord?

Hamlet: Make you a wholesome answer; my wit's diseased:
    but, sir, such answer as I can make, you shall
    command; or, rather, as you say, my mother: therefore,   315
    no more, but to the matter: my mother, you say,—

Rosencrantz: Then thus she says: your behaviour hath struck
    her into amazement and admiration.

Hamlet: O wonderful son, that can so astonish a mother!
    But is there no sequel at the heels of this mother's   320
    admiration? Impart.

Rosencrantz: She desires to speak with you in her closet,
    ere you go to bed.

Hamlet: We shall obey, were she ten times our mother. Have
    you any further trade with us?   325

Rosencrantz: My lord, you once did love me.

Hamlet: So I do still, by these pickers and stealers.

Rosencrantz: Good my lord, what is your cause of distemper?
    You do freely bar the door of your own liberty, if you
    deny your griefs to your friend.   330

Hamlet: Sir, I lack advancement.

Rosencrantz: How can that be, when you have the voice of
    the king himself for your succession in Denmark?

Hamlet: Ay, sir, but "While the grass grows,"—the proverb
    is something musty.   335

[Re-enter Players with recorders.]

    O, the recorders! let me see one. To withdraw with
    you:—why do you go about to recover the wind of me,
    as if you would drive me into a toil?

Guildenstern: O, my lord, if my duty be too bold, my love
    is too unmannerly.   340

Hamlet: I do not well understand that. Will you play upon
    this pipe?

348   *ventages:* openings (on the recorder)

351   *stops:* openings

362   *fret:* annoy or equip with frets (the ridges on a stringed instrument which mark the positions for the finger). Hamlet is playing on the double meaning.

364-372   Hamlet is doing to Polonius what he has just criticized Guildenstern for doing: playing him like an instrument.

375   *to the top of my bent:* to my limit

Guildenstern: My lord, I cannot.

Hamlet: I pray you.

Guildenstern: Believe me, I cannot. 345

Hamlet: I do beseech you.

Guildenstern: I know no touch of it, my lord.

Hamlet: 'Tis as easy as lying: govern these ventages with
your fingers and thumb, give it breath with your mouth,
and it will discourse most excellent music. Look you, 350
these are the stops.

Guildenstern: But these cannot I command to any utterance
of harmony; I have not the skill.

Hamlet: Why, look you now, how unworthy a thing you
make of me! You would play upon me; you would seem 355
to know my stops; you would pluck out the heart of
my mystery; you would sound me from my lowest note
to the top of my compass: and there is much music,
excellent voice, in this little organ; yet cannot you make
it speak. 'Sblood, do you think that I am easier to 360
be played on than a pipe? Call me what instrument you
will, though you can fret me, yet you cannot play
upon me.

[Re-enter Polonius.]

God bless you, sir!

Polonius: My lord, the queen would speak with you, and 365
presently.

Hamlet: Do you see yonder cloud that's almost in shape of
a camel?

Polonius: By the mass, and 'tis like a camel, indeed.

Hamlet: Methinks it is like a weasel. 370

Polonius: It is backed like a weasel.

Hamlet: Or like a whale?

Polonius: Very like a whale.

Hamlet: Then will I come to my mother by and by.
They fool me to the top of my bent. I will come by 375
and by.

Polonius: I will say so. *[Exit Polonius.]*

Hamlet: "By and by" is easily said. Leave me, friends.
[Exeunt Rosencrantz, Guildenstern, Horatio, etc.]
'Tis now the very witching time of night,

381   *Contagion:* disease-bearing mists

385   *Nero:* Nero, the Roman emperor, was rumoured to have put his mother to death.

388   *My tongue and soul in this be hypocrites:* I will not express all the bitterness in my soul.

389   *shent:* put to shame, rebuked

390   *To give them seals:* confirm them (my words) by acting upon them

When churchyards yawn, and hell itself breathes out   380
Contagion to this world: now could I drink hot blood,
And do such bitter business as the day
Would quake to look on. Soft! now to my mother.
O, heart, lose not thy nature; let not ever
The soul of Nero enter this firm bosom: 385
Let me be cruel, not unnatural:
I will speak daggers to her, but use none;
My tongue and soul in this be hypocrites;
How in my words soever she be shent,
To give them seals never, my soul, consent!   [*Exit.*]   390

Act 3, Scene 2: Activities

1. In your group or as a class, make a list of "do's" and "don'ts" of good acting, according to Hamlet. If possible, view one of Hamlet's soliloquies a few times on videotape or DVD and discuss the acting in terms of Hamlet's own standards.

2. Hamlet states that the purpose of drama has always been "to hold, as 'twere, / the mirror up to nature; to show virtue her own / feature, scorn her own image, and the very age and / body of the time his form and pressure" (lines 21–24). In your group, discuss the meaning of Hamlet's words.
   - In your experience of this play so far, do you agree that Shakespeare is "holding the mirror up to nature" in the portrayal of the action and characters?
   - Do you think that drama on television or in movies today does "hold the mirror up to nature"?

3. Write a paragraph paraphrasing Hamlet's words to Horatio (lines 64–76). Compare your work with that of a partner. Then, in pairs, discuss why you think Hamlet is moved to praise Horatio just at this moment. What does Hamlet reveal about his own personality here?

4. In your group, choose one of the following activities:
   - Create a flyer, written by Hamlet, announcing the performance of the play *The Murder of Gonzago*. Try, in a subtle way, to send a threatening message to the King through this announcement.
   - Create a song that would be played as the audience enters the room for the performance of *The Mousetrap*. Consider messages that Hamlet could convey through the lyrics.

5. With a partner, paraphrase the different opinions of the Player King and the Player Queen about faithfulness in love. In your journal, write your own personal response to these ideas.

6. To Hamlet, Claudius' behaviour is conclusive proof of his guilt. However, other people in *The Mousetrap* audience may have had different interpretations of what happened. Divide the class into five groups. Each group should write a diary entry about the performance from the point of view of a different character: Polonius, Ophelia, Gertrude, Rosencrantz, and Lucianus (the actor). Read the diary entries aloud to the class.

7. As a man, whom would you prefer to have as a best friend—Hamlet or Horatio? As a woman, which of the two would you be more likely to fall in love with? In your journal, explain your answer by describing the qualities you admire and those you dislike in each character.

For the next scene . . .

In your journal, write about a time when telling one lie or doing one wrong thing put you in a situation where, to cover your first lie, you had to tell more. What was the outcome, and how did you finally break the cycle of lies? (If this hasn't happened to you, think of a time when it happened to someone you know or know about.)

Act 3, Scene 3

In this scene . . .

Claudius' plans are moving ahead quickly as he prepares Rosencrantz and Guildenstern to accompany Hamlet to England. Then, alone on stage, Claudius struggles with his conscience and tries to pray for forgiveness. He knows, however, that prayer alone will not bring forgiveness if he continues to benefit from his sin. Hamlet enters, sees the King at prayer, and debates with himself whether or not to kill him.

3   *I . . . dispatch:* I will quickly prepare your instructions.

5   *terms of our estate:* my position as king

7   *provide:* prepare

11   *single and peculiar life:* private life of an individual

13   *'noyance:* harm
14   *weal:* welfare
15   *cease of majesty:* death of a king
16   *gulf:* whirlpool
17   *massy:* huge, massive

20   *mortised:* joined (a carpenter's term)
21   *annexment:* addition
22   *Attends the boisterous ruin:* is included in its violent destruction
24   *Arm:* get ready

Scene 3

A room in the same.
Enter King, Rosencrantz, and
Guildenstern.

King: I like him not, nor stands it safe with us
    To let his madness range. Therefore prepare you;
    I your commission will forthwith dispatch,
    And he to England shall along with you:
    The terms of our estate may not endure   5
    Hazard so dangerous as doth hourly grow
    Out of his lunacies.
Guildenstern: We will ourselves provide:
    Most holy and religious fear it is
    To keep those many many bodies safe
    That live and feed upon your majesty.   10
Rosencrantz: The single and peculiar life is bound
    With all the strength and armour of the mind
    To keep itself from 'noyance; but much more
    That spirit upon whose weal depend and rest
    The lives of many. The cease of majesty   15
    Dies not alone, but like a gulf doth draw
    What's near it with it: it is a massy wheel,
    Fix'd on the summit of the highest mount,
    To whose huge spokes ten thousand lesser things
    Are mortised and adjoin'd; which, when it falls,   20
    Each small annexment, petty consequence,
    Attends the boisterous ruin. Never alone
    Did the king sigh, but with a general groan.
King: Arm you, I pray you, to this speedy voyage,
    For we will fetters put upon this fear,   25
    Which now goes too free-footed.
Rosencrantz, Guildenstern: We will haste us.
               [Exeunt Rosencrantz and Guildenstern.]

30	*To hear the process:* to hear what happens; *tax him home:* scold him thoroughly
32	*meet:* appropriate
34	*of vantage:* from an advantageous position, or, in addition
37	*rank:* disgusting
38	*the primal eldest curse:* In the Bible, God cursed Cain for murdering his brother Abel.
43	*in pause:* in doubt
46	*rain:* Rain is traditionally associated with mercy.
47-48	*Whereto serves . . . offence?:* How can mercy act except on a sinner?
49-51	The two purposes of prayer are to prevent sin before it happens or to pardon it afterwards.
57	*offence:* benefits of the crime.
58	*currents:* courses of events
59	*Offence's gilded hand:* the gold-filled hand of the guilty person; *shove by:* push aside
60-61	*the wicked . . . law:* The illegally acquired money can be used to bribe officers of law.
62	*shuffling:* evasion by trickery; *lies:* is exposed

[Enter Polonius.]

Polonius: My lord, he's going to his mother's closet:
    Behind the arras I'll convey myself,
    To hear the process; I'll warrant she'll tax him home: 30
    And, as you said, and wisely was it said,
    'Tis meet that some more audience than a mother,
    Since nature makes them partial, should o'erhear
    The speech, of vantage. Fare you well, my liege:
    I'll call upon you ere you go to bed,   35
    And tell you what I know.
King: Thanks, dear my lord.

                      [Exit Polonius.]

O, my offence is rank, it smells to heaven; It hath the
    primal eldest curse upon't,
A brother's murder. Pray can I not,
Though inclination be as sharp as will: 40
My stronger guilt defeats my strong intent,
And like a man to double business bound,
I stand in pause where I shall first begin,
And both neglect. What if this cursed hand
Were thicker than itself with brother's blood,   45
Is there not rain enough in the sweet heavens
To wash it white as snow? Whereto serves mercy
But to confront the visage of offence?
And what's in prayer but this two-fold force,
To be forestalled ere we come to fall,   50
Or pardon'd being down? Then I'll look up;
My fault is past. But, O, what form of prayer
Can serve my turn? "Forgive me my foul murder"?
That cannot be, since I am still possess'd
Of those effects for which I did the murder,   55
My crown, mine own ambition and my queen.
May one be pardon'd and retain the offence?
In the corrupted currents of this world
Offence's gilded hand may shove by justice,
And oft 'tis seen the wicked prize itself   60
Buys out the law: but 'tis not so above:
There is no shuffling, there the action lies
In his true nature, and we ourselves compell'd

64   *to the teeth and forehead:* to the fullest extent

65   *what rests?:* what remains?

69   *limed soul:* Birds were trapped with birdlime, a sticky substance that was smeared on twigs.

70   *engaged:* entangled; *assay:* an attempt

74   *pat:* easily

76   *That would be scann'd:* That should be considered carefully.

80   *hire and salary:* acting like a hired killer. The implication is that it would not be real revenge.

81   *grossly:* when his sins were unrepented; *full of bread:* not having fasted (in penance)

82   *broad blown:* in full bloom; *flush:* blooming

83   *audit:* account. (The credits and debits would be good and evil deeds.)

84   *in our circumstance . . . thought:* as far as we humans understand

87   *season'd:* prepared

89   *hent:* opportunity

92   *gaming:* gambling

93   *relish:* trace

96   *stays:* waits

97   *physic:* medicine (referring to Claudius' prayers)

Even to the teeth and forehead of our faults
To give in evidence. What then? what rests?   65
Try what repentance can: what can it not?
Yet what can it when one can not repent!
O wretched state! O bosom black as death!
O limed soul, that struggling to be free
Art more engaged! Help, angels! make assay!   70
Bow stubborn knees, and, heart with strings of steel,
Be soft as sinews of the new-born babe!
All may be well!   [*Retires and kneels.*]

[*Enter Hamlet.*]

Hamlet: Now might I do it pat, now he is praying;
And now I'll do't: and so he goes to heaven: 75
And so am I revenged. That would be scann'd:
A villain kills my father; and, for that,
I, his sole son, do this same villain send
To heaven.
O, this is hire and salary, not revenge.   80
He took my father grossly, full of bread,
With all his crimes broad blown, as flush as May;
And how his audit stands who knows save heaven?
But in our circumstance and course of thought,
'Tis heavy with him: and am I then revenged,   85
To take him in the purging of his soul,
When he is fit and season'd for his passage?
No.
Up, sword; and know thou a more horrid hent:
When he is drunk asleep, or in his rage,   90
Or in the incestuous pleasure of his bed,
At gaming, swearing, or about some act
That has no relish of salvation in't:
Then trip him, that his heels may kick at heaven
And that his soul may be as damn'd and black   95
As hell, whereto it goes. My mother stays:
This physic but prolongs thy sickly days.   [*Exit.*]
King [*Rising*]: My words fly up, my thoughts remain below:
Words without thoughts never to heaven go.   [*Exit.*]

Act 3, Scene 3: Activities

1. Write a short news report informing the public that Hamlet is being sent to England. The report could take different forms:

    *   an international news release by the palace press corps. This is intended for an audience in Norway. The readers of this report might be looking for signs of weakness in Denmark's political life.

    *   a tabloid-type article emphasizing the sensational aspects of recent events in the palace. This article should arouse curiosity, appeal to the emotions, and perhaps exaggerate the facts.

    *   a local press release from the palace, to be read aloud outside the palace gates. It should boost allegiance to Claudius, and calm down the people who support Hamlet.

    Begin brainstorming for your news report by listing ten key words that indicate the slant or bias of your communication.

2. Summarize the conflict that Claudius expresses in his prayer. What were your feelings toward Claudius while you were reading his prayer? Do you feel sympathy for him or identify with his predicament because you have experienced a similar conflict yourself? Explain your response in your journal.

3. What are Hamlet's reasons for not killing Claudius? Suggest other reasons, not mentioned by Hamlet, why he is not able to kill Claudius at this time.

4. Both Claudius and Hamlet use imagery that reflects their state of mind. List the images that Claudius and Hamlet use in this scene. Sketch your interpretation of one or two of them, and ask classmates to identify the image(s) that you have sketched. (Instead of sketching, you could create a collage from magazine photos.)

5. With a partner, plan the blocking (the positioning and movement of the actors) in the part of the scene when Hamlet enters and sees Claudius at prayer. Consider these questions:

   - Which character is closer to the audience?
   - How far apart are the two men?
   - In which direction are they facing?
   - Does either of them move?

   Create a sketch of your blocking and compare it with those of others in the class.

6. In groups, discuss this question: At this point in the play, who is the underdog, Hamlet or Claudius? Be prepared to defend your position to others.

For the next scene . . .

Most of us have had, or will have, reason to confront another person and express a lot of anger that we have been storing up. In your journal, make a list of "do's" and "don'ts" about this type of confrontation. Then think of a confrontation you have already experienced. How many of your "do's" and "don'ts" did you follow? If a similar situation were to occur, how would you handle it this time?

Act 3, Scene 4

In this scene . . .

Polonius hides behind a tapestry in the Queen's room just as Hamlet is arriving. When Hamlet speaks harshly to Gertrude, she fears that he might hurt her and she cries out. When Polonius also cries out, Hamlet thinks he has caught Claudius spying and thrusts his sword through the tapestry, killing Polonius. As Hamlet is shaming his mother for marrying Claudius, the Ghost appears to Hamlet. Gertrude, however, cannot see the Ghost and thinks Hamlet must be insane. After Hamlet convinces Gertrude of his own sanity and of her immorality in marrying Claudius, she promises to lie to the King by telling him that Hamlet is indeed mad.

1	*straight:* right away
2	*broad:* unrestrained, extreme
4	*heat:* anger
5	*round:* direct
12	*idle:* silly
15	*rood:* cross
20	*glass:* mirror
25	*for a ducat:* I'll bet a ducat (a gold coin)

Stage direction

(following line 25): *pass:* sword thrust

Scene 4

The Queen's closet.
Enter Queen and Polonius.

Polonius: He will come straight. Look you lay home to him:
　Tell him his pranks have been too broad to bear with,
　And that your grace hath screen'd and stood between
　Much heat and him. I'll silence me e'en here.
　Pray you, be round with him.　　　　　　　　　　　　5
Hamlet [Without]: Mother! mother! mother!
Queen: I'll warrant you; fear me not.
　Withdraw, I hear him coming.
　　　　　　　　　　[*Polonius hides behind the arras.*]

　[*Enter Hamlet.*]

Hamlet: Now, mother; what's the matter?
Queen: Hamlet, thou hast thy father much offended.　　10
Hamlet: Mother, you have my father much offended.
Queen: Come, come, you answer with an idle tongue.
Hamlet: Go, go, you question with a wicked tongue.
Queen: Why, how now, Hamlet?
Hamlet:　　　　　　　　　　　What's the matter now?
Queen: Have you forgot me?
Hamlet:　　　　　　　　　　　No, by the rood, not so:　　15
　You are the queen, your husband's brother's wife;
　And—would it were not so!—you are my mother.
Queen: Nay, then, I'll set those to you that can speak.
Hamlet: Come, come, and sit you down; you shall not budge:
　You go not, till I set you up a glass　　　　　　　　20
　Where you may see the inmost part of you.
Queen: What wilt thou do? thou wilt not murder me?
　Help, help, ho!
Polonius [Behind]: What, ho! help! help! help!
Hamlet [Drawing]: How now! a rat? Dead, for a ducat, dead!　25
　　　　　　　[*Hamlet makes a pass through the arras.*]

30-32	Hamlet is probably not accusing Gertrude of murder. He is combining the two acts of murder and marriage into one, in which Gertrude is implicated. Gertrude, by her response, shows her innocence.
39	*damned custom:* sinful habits; *brass'd it:* covered it (Gertrude's heart) with brass
40	*proof and bulwark:* impenetrable
44	*rose:* symbol of perfection
46	*sets a blister there:* Hamlet is referring to the practice of branding the foreheads of prostitutes.
48	*contraction:* marriage contract
50	*rhapsody of words:* a string of meaningless words
51-53	*this solidity . . . at the act:* Even the earth is sorrowful, as if it were Doomsday.
54	*That roars . . . index?:* that deserves such a violent introduction; *index:* preface
56	*counterfeit presentment:* representation
58	*Hyperion:* sun-god; *front:* forehead
60	*station:* pose, bearing; *Mercury:* messenger of the gods. Mercury represented grace and beauty.
61	*heaven-kissing hill:* Mount Olympus, home of the gods

Polonius [*Behind*]: O, I am slain.   [*Falls and dies.*]
Queen: O me, what hast thou done?
Hamlet: Nay, I know not: is it the king?
Queen: O, what a rash and bloody deed is this!
Hamlet: A bloody deed; almost as bad, good mother,   30
    As kill a king, and marry with his brother.
Queen: "As kill a king!"
Hamlet: Ay, lady, 'twas my word.
             [*Lifts up the arras and sees Polonius.*]
    Thou wretched, rash, intruding fool, farewell!
    I took thee for thy better; take thy fortune:
    Thou find'st to be too busy is some danger.   35
    Leave wringing of your hands: peace! sit you down,
    And let me wring your heart: for so I shall,
    If it be made of penetrable stuff:
    If damned custom have not brass'd it so,
    That it is proof and bulwark against sense.   40
Queen: What have I done, that thou darest wag thy tongue
    In noise so rude against me?
Hamlet: Such an act
    That blurs the grace and blush of modesty,
    Calls virtue hypocrite, takes off the rose
    From the fair forehead of an innocent love,   45
    And sets a blister there; makes marriage vows
    As false as dicers' oaths: O, such a deed
    As from the body of contraction plucks
    The very soul, and sweet religion makes
    A rhapsody of words: heaven's face doth glow;   50
    Yea, this solidity and compound mass,
    With tristful visage, as against the doom,
    Is thought-sick at the act.
Queen: Ay me, what act,
    That roars so loud and thunders in the index?
Hamlet: Look here, upon this picture, and on this,   55
    The counterfeit presentment of two brothers.
    See what a grace was seated on this brow:
    Hyperion's curls; the front of Jove himself,
    An eye like Mars, to threaten and command;
    A station like the herald Mercury   60
    New-lighted on a heaven-kissing hill;

66	*mildew'd ear:* a rotting ear of corn
67	*Blasting:* infecting
68	*leave:* cease
69	*batten:* eat gluttonously
71	*hey-day:* youthful wild spirits; *blood:* Blood was considered the source of sexual desire.
75	*apoplex'd:* paralysed
76-78	*Nor sense . . . difference:* Perception (sense) was never so enslaved (thrall'd) to madness (ecstasy) that it lost all ability to distinguish between things.
79	*cozen'd:* cheated; *hoodman-blind:* blindman's bluff
83	*so mope:* be so dull and stupid
84-87	*Rebellious hell . . . fire:* If middle-aged people can be so given to passion, young people should not be expected to show any self-control.
90	*panders:* caters to, acts as a pimp for
92	*grained:* permanently stained
93	*leave their tinct:* lose their colour
94	*enseamed:* filthy, disgusting

A combination and a form, indeed,
Where every god did seem to set his seal
To give the world assurance of a man:
This was your husband. Look you now, what follows: 65
Here is your husband; like a mildew'd ear,
Blasting his wholesome brother. Have you eyes?
Could you on this fair mountain leave to feed,
And batten on this moor? Ha! have you eyes?
You cannot call it love, for at your age   70
The hey-day in the blood is tame, it's humble,
And waits upon the judgment: and what judgment
Would step from this to this? Sense sure you have,
Else could you not have motion: but sure that sense
Is apoplex'd: for madness would not err,   75
Nor sense to ecstasy was ne'er so thrall'd
But it reserved some quantity of choice,
To serve in such a difference. What devil was't
That thus hath cozen'd you at hoodman-blind?
Eyes without feeling, feeling without sight,   80
Ears without hands or eyes, smelling sans all,
Or but a sickly part of one true sense
Could not so mope.
O shame! where is thy blush? Rebellious hell,
If thou canst mutine in a matron's bones,   85
To flaming youth let virtue be as wax
And melt in her own fire: proclaim no shame
When the compulsive ardour gives the charge,
Since frost itself as actively doth burn,
And reason panders will.
Queen: O Hamlet, speak no more: 90
Thou turn'st mine eyes into my very soul,
And there I see such black and grained spots
As will not leave their tinct.
Hamlet: Nay, but to live
In the rank sweat of an enseamed bed,
Stew'd in corruption, honeying and making love   95
Over the nasty sty—
Queen: O, speak to me no more;
These words like daggers enter in my ears.
No more, sweet Hamlet!

99   *not twentieth part the tithe:* not even a small fraction (a twentieth of one-tenth)

100   *a vice of kings:* an actor playing a king, who combines the qualities of a villain and a clown

101   *cutpurse:* thief

102   *diadem:* crown

104   *A king of shreds and patches:* Multi-coloured rags (shreds and patches) were the costume worn by a professional clown.

107   *he's mad:* The Ghost is not visible to Gertrude, who thinks it is one of Hamlet's hallucinations.

109   *lapsed in time and passion:* having let both time and passion slip away

113   *whet:* sharpen

116   *Conceit:* imagination

120   *incorporal:* without substance

122   *in the alarm:* when the alarm is raised

123   *like life in excrements:* as if your hair were alive ("excrements" means "outgrowths" such as hair and fingernails)

128-129   *His form . . . capable:* His appearance and grievances would even make stones responsive.

130-131   *Lest . . . effects:* for fear that by your look you turn me away from accomplishing my grim purpose

132   *want true colour:* lack courage

Hamlet: A murderer and a villain;
A slave that is not twentieth part the tithe
Of your precedent lord: a vice of kings; 100
A cutpurse of the empire and the rule,
That from a shelf the precious diadem stole
And put it in his pocket!
Queen: No more!
Hamlet: A king of shreds and patches!—

[*Enter Ghost.*]

Save me, and hover o'er me with your wings, 105
You heavenly guards! What would you, gracious figure?
Queen: Alas! he's mad.
Hamlet: Do you not come your tardy son to chide,
That, lapsed in time and passion, lets go by
The important acting of your dread command? 110
O, say!
Ghost: Do not forget: this visitation
Is but to whet thy almost blunted purpose.
But, look! amazement on thy mother sits:
O, step between her and her fighting soul: 115
Conceit in weakest bodies strongest works:
Speak to her, Hamlet.
Hamlet: How is it with you, lady?
Queen: Alas, how is't with you,
That you do bend your eye on vacancy,
And with the incorporal air do hold discourse? 120
Forth at your eyes your spirits wildly peep;
And, as the sleeping soldiers in the alarm,
Your bedded hair, like life in excrements,
Starts up, and stands on end. O gentle son,
Upon the heat and flame of thy distemper 125
Sprinkle cool patience. Whereon do you look?
Hamlet: On him, on him! Look you how pale he glares!
His form and cause conjoin'd, preaching to stones,
Would make them capable. Do not look upon me,
Lest with this piteous action you convert 130
My stern effects: then what I have to do
Will want true colour; tears perchance for blood.
Queen: To whom do you speak this?

139   *coinage:* invention

140-141   *This bodiless . . . in:* Madness can easily create such hallucinations.

145   *And I . . . re-word:* I will repeat my ideas in the same words; or, I will repeat my ideas in different words. Either way would be proof of Hamlet's sanity.

147   *Lay not . . . soul:* don't console yourself by thinking; *unction:* ointment

149-151   *It will but . . . unseen:* It will form a scab over the infected area, while the infection continues spreading underneath.

153   *compost:* manure (which will cause the evil weeds to grow even more)

154   *virtue:* adopting a virtuous or self-righteous tone

155   *pursy:* pudgy, fat

156-157   *Virtue . . . good:* Goodness must bend and beg in order to change evil.

158   *cleft my heart in twin:* broken my heart, or, divided my loyalties

162   *Assume:* pretend

163-167   *That monster . . . put on:* Custom (habitual action) is like a monster in that it destroys our good sense and strengthens our bad behaviour. But custom can also be an angel in that it strengthens good behaviour, just as frequent wearing makes clothes comfortable.

Hamlet: Do you see nothing there?

Queen: Nothing at all; yet all that is I see.

Hamlet: Nor did you nothing hear?

Queen: No, nothing but ourselves. 135

Hamlet: Why, look you there! look, how it steals away!
    My father, in his habit as he lived!
    Look, where he goes, even now, out at the portal!

                                        [*Exit Ghost.*]

Queen: This is the very coinage of your brain:
    This bodiless creation ecstasy   140
    Is very cunning in.

Hamlet: Ecstasy!
    My pulse, as yours, does temperately keep time,
    And makes as healthful music: it is not madness
    That I have utter'd: bring me to the test,
    And I the matter will re-word, which madness   145
    Would gambol from. Mother, for love of grace,
    Lay not that flattering unction to your soul,
    That not your trespass but my madness speaks:
    It will but skin and film the ulcerous place,
    While rank corruption, mining all within,   150
    Infects unseen. Confess yourself to heaven;
    Repent what's past, avoid what is to come,
    And do not spread the compost on the weeds,
    To make them ranker. Forgive me this my virtue,
    For in the fatness of these pursy times   155
    Virtue itself of vice must pardon beg,
    Yea, curb and woo for leave to do him good.

Queen: O Hamlet! thou hast cleft my heart in twain.

Hamlet: O throw away the worser part of it,
    And live the purer with the other half.   160
    Good night: But go not to my uncle's bed.
    Assume a virtue, if you have it not.
    That monster, custom, who all sense doth eat,
    Oft habit's devil, is angel yet in this,
    That to the use of actions fair and good   165
    He likewise gives a frock or livery,
    That aptly is put on. Refrain to-night,
    And that shall lend a kind of easiness
    To the next abstinence: the next more easy;

170   *For use . . . nature:* Forming a new habit can change an ingrained quality.

177   *their scourge and minister:* the instrument and the agent of heaven's punishment (i.e., both the lash and the wielder of the lash)

178   *bestow:* dispose of

185   *wanton:* lewdly

188   *ravel:* unravel, explain

192   *paddock:* toad; *gib:* tomcat. The toad, bat and tomcat were associated with witchcraft.

193   *dear concernings:* important matters

195-196   *Unpeg the basket . . . fly:* give away secrets

197   *To try conclusions:* to repeat the experiment

206   *sweep my way:* clear my path

For use almost can change the stamp of nature,   170
And either master the devil, or throw him out
With wondrous potency. Once more, good night:
And when you are desirous to be blest,
I'll blessing beg of you. For this same lord,
                          [*Pointing to Polonius.*]
I do repent: but heaven hath pleased it so,   175
To punish me with this, and this with me,
That I must be their scourge and minister.
I will bestow him, and will answer well
The death I gave him. So, again, good night.
I must be cruel, only to be kind: 180
Thus bad begins, and worse remains behind.
One more word, good lady.
Queen: What shall I do?
Hamlet: Not this, by no means, that I bid you do:
Let the bloat king tempt you again to bed;
Pinch wanton on your cheek; call you his mouse;   185
And let him, for a pair of reechy kisses,
Or paddling in your neck with his damn'd fingers,
Make you to ravel all this matter out,
That I essentially am not in madness,
But mad in craft. 'Twere good you let him know;   190
For who, that's but a queen, fair, sober, wise,
Would from a paddock, from a bat, a gib,
Such dear concernings hide? who would do so?
No, in despite of sense and secrecy,
Unpeg the basket on the house's top,   195
Let the birds fly, and, like the famous ape,
To try conclusions, in the basket creep,
And break your own neck down.
Queen: Be thou assured if words be made of breath,
And breath of life, I have no life to breathe   200
What thou hast said to me.
Hamlet: I must to England; you know that?
Queen: Alack,
I had forgot: 'tis so concluded on.
Hamlet: There's letters sealed: and my two schoolfellows,
Whom I will trust as I will adders fang'd,   205
They bear the mandate; they must sweep my way,

207   *marshal me to knavery:* make me suffer from their foolishness, or lead me on to evil

208   *engineer:* maker of engines (bombs)

209   *Hoist with his own petar:* blown up by his own bomb

212   *When in one . . . meet:* when two schemes collide

213   *This man:* i.e., Polonius; *set me packing:* hasten by departure

216   *grave:* another pun

217   *prating:* foolish

218   *to draw toward an end:* to finish my business. There is a play on "draw," which also means "drag."

And marshal me to knavery. Let it work,
For 'tis the sport to have the engineer
Hoist with his own petar: and't shall go hard
But I will delve one yard below their mines,   210
And blow them at the moon: O, 'tis most sweet,
When in one line two crafts directly meet.
This man shall set me packing.
I'll lug the guts into the neighbour room.
Mother, good night. Indeed, this counsellor   215
Is now most still, most secret and most grave,
Who was in life a foolish prating knave.
Come, sir, to draw toward an end with you.
Good night, mother.
                    [*Exeunt severally: Hamlet dragging out the
                                    body of Polonius.*]

Act 3, Scene 4: Activities

1. In your group, plan a short segment of a radio or television advice call-in show. Just before Hamlet arrives in Gertrude's room, she is calling for advice about how to behave with him. Present Gertrude's question and the expert's response to the class.

2. In a group of three, prepare lines 6–23 for dramatic reading to the class. One person will be Hamlet, another Gertrude, and the third will be an acting coach. The class should decide which readings were the most effective and discuss what made them effective.

3. This scene has revealed contradictions in Hamlet's character:

   • He has hesitated and delayed in killing Claudius for months, yet when he thinks Claudius is hiding behind the curtain, he thrusts his sword immediately, intending to kill him.

   • His Ghost father tells him to "step between [his mother] and her fighting soul" (line 115), yet Hamlet continues to badger Gertrude.

   • He shows no remorse for killing Polonius, and calls him a "wretched, rash, intruding fool" (line 33).

   You have been a witness to this scene. Choose one of the above scenarios and write a frank letter to Hamlet, commenting on his behaviour and giving him advice. Has your opinion about him changed?

4. Suppose that the Ghost had appeared to both Gertrude and Hamlet, and that it had spoken for a longer time to each of them.

   • Write the speech that the Ghost might have given to Gertrude.

   • Write the speech that the Ghost might have given to Hamlet.

   • As a class, listen to some of the speeches and discuss whether the added comments might have influenced Hamlet's or Gertrude's subsequent behaviour.

5. As a class, locate examples of imagery that Hamlet uses in his confrontation with his mother. Do you think that the imagery is persuasive?

6. Since Gertrude cannot see the Ghost, we are free to decide if the Ghost really appears in the room, or if it is a figment of Hamlet's overexcited imagination. If you were directing this scene, which would you choose? What are your reasons?

7. As a class, choose five dramatic lines in this scene. Divide the class into five groups. Each group should create a tableau representing one of these lines. (A tableau is a frozen picture in which the characters are caught in mid-action. Their facial expressions and gestures reveal their personality, emotions, and relationships.) Those not participating in the tableau could guess which line is being presented.

8. Choose one of these activities:

   - Write a diary entry that Gertrude might have written after the events of this scene.

   - Write an obituary for Polonius, to be published in the Danish national newspaper.

Act 3: Consider the Whole Act

1. Divide the class into eight small groups, with each group assigned to a part of Act 3:
   - the "To be, or not to be" soliloquy (III, i, 57–89)
   - the nunnery scene (III, i, 90–151)
   - Hamlet's advice to the players (III, i, 1–45)
   - Hamlet's speech to Horatio (III, ii, 55–86)
   - *The Mousetrap* scene (III, ii, 94–265)
   - the prayer scene (III, iii, 37–99)
   - the closet scene (III, iv, 1–35)
   - the portrait scene (III, iv, 36–219, excluding references to the murder of Polonius)

   Each group should review its scene and prepare a report about Hamlet's behaviour, considering both positive and negative aspects of it. Decide whether Act 3 generally presents Hamlet in a positive or negative light. Be ready to support your opinion.

2. The "dumb show" (III, ii, 134–265), provides an opportunity for a director to display his or her creativity and to entertain an audience. In a group, prepare your version of the dumb show. Decide whether you want to include features such as choreography, make-up, masks, or props in your performance. Present your show to the class.

3. Choose one of the following characters: Hamlet, Gertrude, Claudius, Polonius, or Ophelia. Suppose you are acting this role, and the director has asked you to choose one prop or piece of clothing to use during rehearsals in order to either look or feel the part. What would you choose, and why?

4. When Hamlet first heard about his father's murder, he said, "Haste me to know't; that I, with wings as swift / As meditation or the thoughts of love, / May sweep to my revenge" (I, v, 29–31). In your group, list the obstacles both in Hamlet's personality and in his situation that have

prevented him from killing Claudius. Create your own visual interpretation (for example, a drawing, a cartoon, or a collage) of the obstacles.

5. With your group or the whole class, view a scene or segment of Act 3 from a video or DVD of *Hamlet*. Discuss your impressions of the following:

- the setting and costumes
- music
- camera angles and types of shots
- new insights that you did not get when you read the text
- anything that surprised you
- anything you would have done differently as a director of this scene

6. Many lines from this Act have become famous on their own, for example:

- "The undiscover'd country from whose bourn / no traveller returns" (III, i, 80–81)
- "To be, or not to be: that is the question" (III, i, 57)
- "O limed soul, that struggling to be free / Art more engaged!" (III, iii, 69–70)
- "O, what a rash and bloody deed is this!" (III, i, 57)

Try to identify other famous lines with your group. Choose one and create a portfolio of photographs or drawings that illustrate it. You could gather the visuals from other sources or make your own.

7. Find a personality description for each sign of the zodiac (horoscope), and decide which sign suits each of the main characters in the play.

For the next scene . . .

With the class, discuss your opinions about whether banishment is a suitable punishment for a serious violent crime.

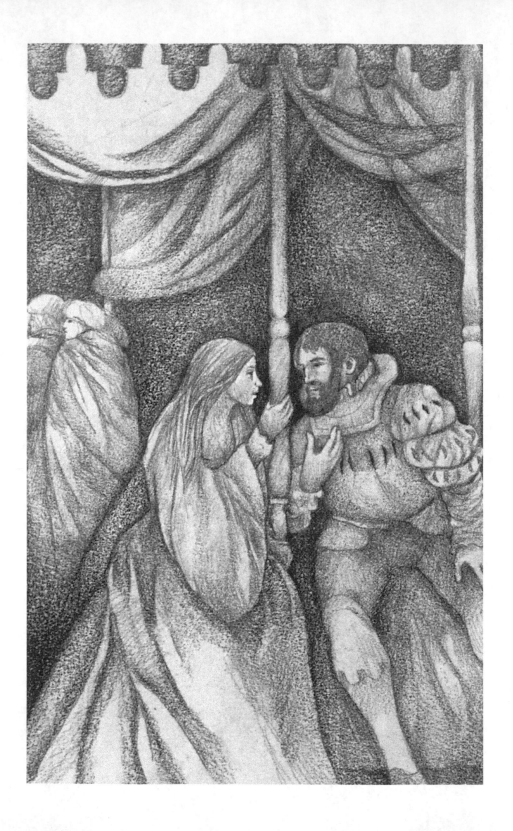

Act 4, Scene 1
In this scene . . .

Gertrude reports Polonius' death to Claudius. She also
follows through on her promise to Hamlet by confirming
that he is mad. Claudius resolves to send Hamlet away
to England immediately. He sends Rosencrantz and
Guildenstern to recover Polonius' body and then
departs with Gertrude to meet with their advisers.

2   *translate:* interpret

11   *brainish apprehension:* brainsick state of mind

16   *answer'd:* explained

17   *providence:* foresight

18   *kept short:* kept under control; *out of haunt:* away from others

21-23   Note the disease imagery that Claudius is using.

22   *divulging:* becoming public knowledge

23   *pith:* vital substance

25   *ore:* precious metal, e.g., gold

26   *Among a mineral:* in a mine

27   *he weeps for what is done:* Is this the truth, or Gertrude's invention?

Act 4, Scene 1

The same.
Enter King, Queen, Rosencrantz,
and Guildenstern.

King: There's matter in these sighs, these profound heaves:
    You must translate: 'tis fit we understand them.
    Where is your son?
Queen: Bestow this place on us a little while.
                     [*Exeunt Rosencrantz and Guildenstern.*]
    Ah, mine own lord, what have I seen to-night! 5
King: What, Gertrude? How does Hamlet?
Queen: Mad as the sea and wind, when both contend
    Which is the mightier: in his lawless fit,
    Behind the arras hearing something stir,
    He whips his rapier out, and cries, "A rat! a rat!" 10
    And in this brainish apprehension kills
    The unseen good old man.
King: O heavy deed!
    It had been so with us, had we been there.
    His liberty is full of threats to all,
    To you yourself, to us, to every one. 15
    Alas, how shall this bloody deed be answer'd?
    It will be laid to us, whose providence
    Should have kept short, restrain'd and out of haunt,
    This mad young man: but so much was our love,
    We would not understand what was most fit, 20
    But, like the owner of a foul disease,
    To keep it from divulging, let it feed
    Even on the pith of life. Where is he gone?
Queen: To draw apart the body he hath kill'd:
    O'er whom his very madness, like some ore 25
    Among a mineral of metals base,
    Shows itself pure; he weeps for what is done.

32   *countenance:* sanction, justify

33   *join you with some further aid:* get some help

36   *speak fair:* speak courteously (so as not to anger)

40   *haply:* perhaps

40-44   Claudius is expressing the hope that he will escape blame
            for Polonius' murder.

42   *level:* straight to the mark; *blank:* bull's eye

44   *woundless:* invulnerable

King: O, Gertrude, come away!
    The sun no sooner shall the mountains touch,
    But we will ship him hence: and this vile deed   30
    We must, with all our majesty and skill,
    Both countenance and excuse. Ho, Guildenstern!

[Re-enter Rosencrantz and Guildenstern.]

    Friends both, go join you with some further aid:
    Hamlet in madness hath Polonius slain,
    And from his mother's closet hath he dragg'd him: 35
    Go seek him out; speak fair, and bring the body
    Into the chapel. I pray you, haste in this.

          [Exeunt Rosencrantz and Guildenstern.]

Come, Gertrude, we'll call up our wisest friends;
    And let them know, both what we mean to do,
    And what's untimely done: so, haply, slander,   40
    Whose whisper o'er the world's diameter
    As level as the cannon to his blank
    Transports his poisoned shot, may miss our name
    And hit the woundless air. O come away!
    My soul is full of discord and dismay.   *[Exeunt.]*   45

Act 4, Scene 1: Activities

1. In lines 1–32, both Gertrude and Claudius are pretending to some extent. After each of their speeches, write what you think their inner thoughts would be.

2. Claudius voices a number of fears in this scene. Make a list of all his fears. What do you think he really fears the most? How would you list his priorities as King?

For the next scene . . .

If you overheard a conversation in which one person called the other a "sponge," what would you think it meant?

Act 4, Scene 2

In this scene . . .

Rosencrantz and Guildenstern try to find out from Hamlet where Polonius' body is hidden. Hamlet refuses to tell them. When they say he must go with them to Claudius, Hamlet leads them on a chase.

7	*Compounded:* mixed

12	*counsel:* secrets
13	*to be demanded of:* to be questioned by; *replication:* reply

16	*countenance:* favour
17	*authorities:* influence

24	*knavish:* wicked
28-29	*The body . . . body:* This statement could be taken as an expression of Hamlet's madness. As well, Hamlet could mean that Polonius' body is with old King Hamlet, but King Claudius is not (yet) dead.
29-31	*The king . . . Of nothing:* Is Hamlet warning Rosencrantz and Guildenstern about Claudius' fate?
31	*Hide fox . . . after:* Hamlet turns the search for Polonius' body into a game.

Scene 2

Another room in the castle.
Enter Hamlet.

Hamlet: Safely stowed—
Rosencrantz, etc. [*Without*]: Hamlet! lord Hamlet!
Hamlet: But soft, what noise? who calls on Hamlet?
    O, here they come.

[*Enter Rosencrantz and Guildenstern.*]

Rosencrantz: What have you done, my lord, with the dead   5
    body?
Hamlet: Compounded it with dust, whereto 'tis kin.
Rosencrantz: Tell us where 'tis, that we may take it thence
    And bear it to the chapel.
Hamlet: Do not believe it.   10
Rosencrantz: Believe what?
Hamlet: That I can keep your counsel and not mine own.
    Besides, to be demanded of a sponge! what replication
    should be made by the son of a king?
Rosencrantz: Take you me for a sponge, my lord?   15
Hamlet: Ay, sir; that soaks up the king's countenance, his
    rewards, his authorities: but such officers do the king
    best service in the end: he keeps them, like an ape
    doth nuts, in the corner of his jaw; first mouthed, to
    be last swallowed: when he needs what you have   20
    gleaned, it is but squeezing you, and, sponge, you shall
    be dry again.
Rosencrantz: I understand you not, my lord.
Hamlet: I am glad of it: a knavish speech sleeps in a foolish
    ear.   25
Rosencrantz: My lord, you must tell us where the body is,
    and go with us to the king.
Hamlet: The body is with the king, but the king is not with
    the body. The king is a thing—
Guildenstern: A thing, my lord?   30
Hamlet: Of nothing: bring me to him. Hide fox, and all
    after.   [*Exeunt.*]

Act 4, Scene 2: Activities

1. An analogy is an extended comparison of two things that are alike in some respects. In this scene, Hamlet uses the analogy of a sponge to describe Rosencrantz. Suggest other analogies that could be used to describe people like Rosencrantz and Guildenstern. What analogy could you use to describe Hamlet? Form groups and share your ideas.

2. With a partner, create a dialogue between Rosencrantz and Guildenstern immediately after their conversation with Hamlet in this scene. Perform your dialogue for the class.

For the next scene . . .

Sometimes people find themselves laughing or joking about serious or even tragic events. How would you explain this unexpected response? Have you ever found yourself in this situation? Find out what others in the class think, then form your own explanation of this behaviour.

Act 4, Scene 3
In this scene . . .

Hamlet is brought before Claudius and eventually reveals where Polonius' body is hidden. Claudius informs Hamlet that he must go to England for his own safety. Once Claudius is alone, he reveals his plan to send the King of England a letter containing instructions to kill Hamlet as soon as he reaches England.

4	*of:* by; *distracted:* irrational
5	*Who like not . . . eyes:* who judge by appearances, not by reason
6	*scourge:* punishment
7	*To bear . . . even:* to make everything go smoothly
9	*Deliberate pause:* the result of careful consideration
10	*appliance:* remedy
20-23	These lines reveal Hamlet's new preoccupation with the grisly details of death and physical decay.
21	*convocation:* gathering; *politic:* shrewd, busy in statecraft

Scene 3

Another room in the castle.
Enter King, attended.

King: I have sent to seek him, and to find the body.
How dangerous is it that this man goes loose!
Yet must not we put the strong law on him:
He's loved of the distracted multitude,
Who like not in their judgment, but their eyes;   5
And where 'tis so, the offender's scourge is weigh'd,
But never the offence. To bear all smooth and even,
This sudden sending him away must seem
Deliberate pause: diseases desperate grown
By desperate appliance are relieved,   10
Or not at all.

[Enter Rosencrantz.]

         How now? what hath befall'n?
Rosencrantz: Where the dead body is bestow'd, my lord,
We cannot get from him.
King: But where is he?
Rosencrantz: Without, my lord, guarded, to know your
    pleasure.
King: Bring him before us.   15
Rosencrantz: Ho, Guildenstern! bring in my lord.

[Enter Hamlet and Guildenstern.]

King: Now, Hamlet, where's Polonius?
Hamlet: At supper.
King: At supper! Where?
Hamlet: Not where he eats, but where he is eaten: a certain   20
    convocation of politic worms are e'en at him. Your
    worm is your only emperor for diet: we fat all
    creatures else to fat us, and we fat ourselves for

25   *variable service:* different courses

32   *progress:* royal journey

34   *messenger:* Why would Claudius have to send a messenger to heaven?

42   *which we do tender:* which we are concerned about

45   *at help:* favourable
46   *tend:* are waiting; *bent:* ready

49   *I see . . . them:* There is a little angel who knows your plans and tells me of them.

55   *at foot:* closely

58   *leans on:* depends on

maggots: your fat king and your lean beggar is but
variable service, two dishes, but to one table: that's   25
the end.
King: Alas, alas!
Hamlet: A man may fish with the worm that hath eat of a
king, and eat of the fish that hath fed of that worm.
King: What dost thou mean by this?   30
Hamlet: Nothing but to show you how a king may go a
progress through the guts of a beggar.
King: Where is Polonius?
Hamlet: In heaven: send thither to see: if your messenger
find him not there, seek him i' the other place   35
yourself. But indeed, if you find him not within this
month, you shall nose him as you go up the stairs into
the lobby.
King: Go seek him there.   [*To some Attendants.*]
Hamlet: He will stay till you come.   40

[*Exeunt Attendants.*]

King: Hamlet, this deed, for thine especial safety,
Which we do tender, as we dearly grieve
For that which thou hast done, must send thee hence
With fiery quickness: therefore prepare thyself;
The bark is ready and the wind at help,   45
The associates tend, and everything is bent
For England.
Hamlet: For England?
King: Ay, Hamlet.
Hamlet: Good.
King: So is it, if thou knew'st our purposes.
Hamlet: I see a cherub that sees them. But, come; for
England! Farewell, dear mother.   50
King: Thy loving father, Hamlet.
Hamlet: My mother: father and mother is man and wife;
man and wife is one flesh, and so, my mother. Come,
for England!   [*Exit.*]
King: Follow him at foot; tempt him with speed aboard;   55
Delay it not; I'll have him hence to-night:
Away! for everything is seal'd and done
That else leans on the affair: pray you, make haste.

[*Exeunt Rosencrantz and Guildenstern.*]

59	*England:* King of England; *thou hold'st at aught:* you value at all
61	*cicatrice:* scar
62-63	*thy free . . . us:* Although England was not occupied by Danish troops, it still paid tribute to Denmark.
63	*coldly set:* view with indifference
64	*process:* plan
65	*conjuring:* urging, ordering
66	*present:* immediate
67	*hectic:* fever
69	*Howe'er my haps:* whatever happens to me

And England, if my love thou hold'st at aught—
As my great power thereof may give thee sense,   60
Since yet thy cicatrice looks raw and red
After the Danish sword, and thy free awe
Pays homage to us—thou may'st not coldly set
Our sovereign process; which imports at full,
By letters conjuring to that effect,   65
The present death of Hamlet. Do it, England;
For like the hectic in my blood he rages,
And thou must cure me: till I know 'tis done,
Howe'er my haps, my joys were ne'er begun.

                                        [*Exit.*]

Act 4, Scene 3: Activities

1. Hamlet's references to Polonius' already decaying body (lines 17–38) reflect a new mood—one in which he contemplates death in terms of rot and decay. Nevertheless, Hamlet expresses his thoughts humorously. Why have Hamlet's thoughts taken such a macabre turn at this point in the play? Is this change consistent with what we already know about Hamlet?

2. With a partner, read the conversation between the King and Hamlet (lines 17–40). In your opinion, who demonstrates that he has more power in this conversation? How does he communicate that power?

3. Black humour is a type of comedy in which disturbing subjects such as death, disease, or war are treated in a way that is bitter and funny at the same time.

   - As a class, discuss familiar examples of black humour in today's television shows or movies. Is it simply a shocking kind of humour, or is there some message behind it?

   - In your journal, reflect on Hamlet's use of black humour in his comments about Polonius. Is this another aspect of his antic disposition? Does it demonstrate some change in Hamlet's state of mind?

For the next scene . . .

In your journal, reflect on a situation where you took a
strong stand on principle about an issue that other
people did not think was important. What did you gain
or lose by doing this?

Act 4, Scene 4

In this scene . . .

This outdoor scene takes place as Hamlet and Rosencrantz and Guildenstern are about to embark for England. On a plain near the seashore, Fortinbras and his army walk by. One of Fortinbras' captains tells Hamlet about their military campaign, in which thousands of soldiers have died to protect Norway's honour. Hamlet is deeply moved and, in a soliloquy, he criticizes his own inaction by comparing himself with Fortinbras.

3   *conveyance:* carrying out

6   *express . . . eye:* pay our respects in his presence

8   *softly:* slowly

9   *powers:* troops

10   *How purposed?:* What is their destination?

14   *the main of Poland:* all of Poland

16   *with no addition:* without exaggeration

19   *five ducats:* a small sum of money; *farm:* rent

21   *ranker rate:* higher value; *sold in fee:* sold outright (rather than leased)

25   *Will not debate . . . straw:* will not be enough to settle the argument over this thing of little value

26   *imposthume:* abscess (a sore full of pus)

Scene 4

A plain in Denmark.
Enter Fortinbras, and Forces
marching.

Fortinbras: Go, captain, from me greet the Danish king;
    Tell him, that by his licence Fortinbras
    Claims the conveyance of a promised march
    Over his kingdom. You know the rendezvous.
    If that his majesty would aught with us,   5
    We shall express our duty in his eye:
    And let him know so.
Captain: I will do't, my lord.
Fortinbras: Go softly on.   *[Exeunt Fortinbras and Forces.]*

[Enter Hamlet, Rosencrantz, Guildenstern, and others.]

Hamlet: Good sir, whose powers are these?
Captain: They are of Norway, sir.
Hamlet: How purposed, sir, I pray you?   10
Captain: Against some part of Poland.
Hamlet: Who commands them, sir?
Captain: The nephew to old Norway, Fortinbras.
Hamlet: Goes it against the main of Poland, sir,
    Or for some frontier?   15
Captain: Truly to speak, and with no addition,
    We go to gain a little patch of ground
    That hath in it no profit but the name.
    To pay five ducats, five, I would not farm it;
    Nor will it yield to Norway or the Pole   20
    A ranker rate, should it be sold in fee.
Hamlet: Why, then the Polack never will defend it.
Captain: Yes, it is already garrison'd.
Hamlet: Two thousand souls and twenty thousand ducats
    Will not debate the question of this straw: 25
    This is the imposthume of much wealth and peace,
    That inward breaks, and shows no cause without
    Why the man dies. I humbly thank you, sir.

31   *occasions:* happenings; *inform against me:* accuse me

33   *market:* employment, use

35   *discourse:* intelligence

36   *Looking before and after:* able to think about both past and future

38   *fust:* become musty, full of mould

39   *Bestial oblivion:* animal-like forgetfulness; *craven scruple:* cowardly hesitation

40   *event:* outcome

41   *quarter'd:* divided into four, analyzed

44   *Sith:* since

46   *charge:* cost

47   *delicate:* not robust; *tender:* young

49   *Makes mouths at:* mocks; *invisible event:* unknown outcome

52-55   *Rightly to be great . . . stake:* True greatness is *not* fighting over unimportant things; it *is* being ready to fight, even over a small issue, if it is a question of honour.

53   *argument:* cause

57   *blood:* emotions

60   *trick:* trifle (small amount)

62   *Whereon . . . the cause:* not big enough to hold all those who fight for it

63   *continent:* container

Captain: God be wi' you, sir.   [*Exit Captain.*]
Rosencrantz: Will't please you go, my lord?
Hamlet: I'll be with you straight. Go a little before.   30
                              [*Exeunt all but Hamlet.*]
How all occasions do inform against me,
And spur my dull revenge! What is a man,
If his chief good and market of his time
Be but to sleep and feed? a beast, no more.
Sure, he that made us with such large discourse,   35
Looking before and after, gave us not
That capability and godlike reason
To fust in us unused. Now, whether it be
Bestial oblivion, or some craven scruple
Of thinking too precisely on the event, —   40
A thought which, quarter'd, hath but one part wisdom,
And ever three parts coward,—I do not know
Why yet I live to say, "this thing's to do,"
Sith I have cause, and will, and strength, and means,
To do't. Examples gross as earth exhort me: 45
Witness this army, of such mass and charge,
Led by a delicate and tender prince,
Whose spirit, with divine ambition puff'd
Makes mouths at the invisible event,
Exposing what is mortal and unsure   50
To all that fortune, death, and danger dare,
Even for an egg-shell. Rightly to be great
Is not to stir without great argument,
But greatly to find quarrel in a straw
When honour's at the stake. How stand I then,   55
That have a father kill'd, a mother stain'd,
Excitements of my reason and my blood,
And let all sleep, while to my shame I see
The imminent death of twenty thousand men,
That for a fantasy and trick of fame   60
Go to their graves like beds, fight for a plot
Whereon the numbers cannot try the cause,
Which is not tomb enough and continent
To hide the slain? O, from this time forth,
My thoughts be bloody, or be nothing worth!   65
                              [*Exit.*]

Act 4, Scene 4: Activities

1 . In pairs, create a short scene between Horatio and Hamlet, just as Hamlet is leaving Denmark. What would Hamlet want to tell Horatio? What advice might Horatio give?

2. Compare Hamlet's soliloquy beginning with "How all occasions do inform against me" (IV, iv 31–65) with the soliloquy "O, what a rogue and peasant slave am I!" (II, ii, 545–603). In your comparison, consider these questions:

    • What is the immediate cause of each soliloquy?

    • To whom is Hamlet comparing himself, and why?

    • How does Hamlet explain his inaction?

    • What are Hamlet's mood and tone?

    • How does each soliloquy end?

    After comparing the soliloquies, decide in which soliloquy Hamlet's determination to complete his revenge is stronger. Share your opinion with the class.

3. Hamlet admires Fortinbras because he is willing to fight heroically for a small issue when his country's honour is at stake. Discuss whether you think Fortinbras' behaviour would still be considered heroic today. In your journal, complete the following statement in a few sentences: "A hero is someone . . ."

4. In your group, discuss how you would stage this scene so that it provides a contrast in mood and setting to the intensity of the past few scenes. Decide what kind of stage you would be working with, and consider lighting, backdrop, costuming, and movement.

For the next scene . . .

In your journal, write about a time when you gave or received a gift that had special symbolic value that was understood by you and by the other person. (If you have not had this experience, write about a symbolic gift you would like to give to someone.)

Act 4, Scene 5

In this scene . . .

Hamlet's murder of Polonius has had serious repercussions. Ophelia has suffered a serious mental breakdown. At the beginning of the scene, she appears, singing songs and making allusions which seem to make no sense, but which in fact do tell her story. Not yet aware of his sister's madness, Laertes storms into the palace demanding vengeance on Claudius, who he thinks was responsible for Polonius' murder. After the King calms Laertes down, Ophelia re-enters, and Laertes is overwhelmed with grief over her madness. Claudius leads Laertes away to talk in private about the circumstances of Polonius' death. He hints that he will help Laertes avenge his father.

1	*her:* Ophelia
2	*importunate:* insistent; *distract:* out of her mind

6	*Spurns enviously at straws:* gets upset over small things
7	*nothing:* without meaning
8-9	*Yet . . . collection:* Yet its incoherence encourages listeners to draw their own conclusions.
9	*aim at it:* make suggestions as to what it means
10	*And botch . . . thoughts:* clumsily attempt to interpret (Ophelia's) words according to their own ideas
11	*Which:* refers to "words"; *yield:* reveal
11-13	*Which . . . unhappily:* Her words and gestures give the impression that she has experienced some great misfortune.
15	*ill-breeding:* mischief-making
18	*toy:* small event; *amiss:* disaster
19-20	*So full . . . spilt:* A guilty person can be so afraid of revealing his guilt that he does reveal it in the same way that a person who is nervous about spilling the contents of a glass will spill them.
23-66	Ophelia, whose mind has become disoriented, sings songs about death and lost love.
25	*cockle hat:* A cockle hat represents a pilgrim. A lover might describe himself as a pilgrim worshipping his lady.
26	*shoon:* shoes

Scene 5

Elsinore. A room in the castle.
Enter Queen, Horatio, and a
Gentleman.

Queen: I will not speak with her.
Horatio: She is importunate, indeed distract:
  Her mood will needs be pitied.
Queen: What would she have?
Horatio: She speaks much of her father, says, she hears
  There's tricks i' the world, and hems and beats her heart,   5
  Spurns enviously at straws; speaks things in doubt,
  That carry but half sense: her speech is nothing,
  Yet the unshaped use of it doth move
  The hearers to collection; they aim at it,
  And botch the words up fit to their own thoughts;   10
  Which, as her winks and nods and gestures yield them,
  Indeed would make one think there would be thought,
  Though nothing sure, yet much unhappily.
  'Twere good she were spoken with, for she may strew
  Dangerous conjectures in ill-breeding minds.   15
Queen: Let her come in.   *[Exit Gentleman.]*
  [Aside.] To my sick soul, as sin's true nature is,
  Each toy seems prologue to some great amiss:
  So full of artless jealousy is guilt,
  It spills itself in fearing to be spilt.   20

  [Re-enter Gentleman with Ophelia.]

Ophelia: Where is the beauteous majesty of Denmark?
Queen: How now, Ophelia?

Ophelia [Sings]:   How should I your true love know
                From another one?
            By his cockle hat and staff,   25
                And his sandal shoon.

27   *imports:* is the meaning of

31   *turf:* clump of earth

37   *Larded:* decorated

39   *showers:* tears

41   *God'ield you!:* May God reward you.

41-42   *They say . . . daughter:* An old legend told of a baker's daughter who was changed into an owl when she scolded her mother for giving bread to Jesus.

44   *Conceit:* imaginative thoughts

47   *Saint Valentine's day:* According to tradition, the first person seen on St. Valentine's day would be a true love.

52   *dupp'd:* opened

57   *By Gis:* By Jesus

59   *Young men will do't:* Young men will seduce maidens.

60   *By cock:* By God

Queen: Alas, sweet lady, what imports this song?
Ophelia: Say you? nay, pray you, mark.

      [*Sings*]: He is dead and gone, lady,
                He is dead and gone;   30
            At his head a grass-green turf,
                At his heels a stone.

  Oh, oh!
Queen: Nay, but Ophelia,—
Ophelia: Pray you, mark.

      [*Sings*]: White his shroud as the mountain snow.   35

  [*Enter King.*]

Queen: Alas, look here, my lord.
Ophelia [*Sings*]:   Larded with sweet flowers;
             Which bewept to the grave did go
                With true-love showers.
King: How do you, pretty lady?   40
Ophelia: Well, God'ield you! They say the owl was a baker's
    daughter. Lord, we know what we are, but know not
    what we may be. God be at your table!
King: Conceit upon her father.
Ophelia: Pray you, let us have no words of this; but when   45
    they ask you what it means, say you this:

      [*Sings*]: To-morrow is Saint Valentine's day,
             All in the morning betime,
          And I a maid at your window,
             To be your Valentine.   50

          Then up he rose, and donn'd his clothes,
             And dupp'd the chamber-door;
          Let in the maid, that out a maid
             Never departed more.

King: Pretty Ophelia!   55
Ophelia: Indeed, la, without an oath, I'll make an end on't:

      [*Sings*]: By Gis, and by Saint Charity,
             Alack, and fie for shame!
          Young men will do't if they come to't,
             By cock, they are to blame.   60

61	*tumbled me:* made love to me
65	*And:* if
76-77	*they come not . . . battalias:* The image is of an army of sorrows. An equivalent modern expression would be, "It never rains, but it pours."
79	*muddied:* confused. The image is of a pond whose muddy bottom has been stirred up.
80	*Thick:* confused, unclear
81	*greenly:* foolishly, like an unskilled youth
82	*In hugger-mugger:* secretly
84	*pictures:* outward forms (without souls)
87	*Feeds . . . clouds:* is filled with bewilderment and keeps his intentions secret
88	*wants not buzzers:* does not lack gossipers
89	*pestilent:* poisonous
90-92	*Wherein necessity . . . ear:* Because the gossipers have no definite information about Polonius' death, they will accuse Claudius.
92	*this:* i.e., all these problems
93	*murdering-piece:* a cannon that scatters its shot, hitting many targets at once
94	*superfluous death:* more than one death
95	*Switzers:* Swiss mercenary soldiers who were used as palace guards

> Quoth she, before you tumbled me,
> You promised me to wed.

He answers:

> So would I ha' done, by yonder sun,
> And thou hadst not come to my bed.   65

King: How long has she been thus?
Ophelia: I hope all will be well. We must be patient: but I
    cannot choose but weep, to think they should lay him
    i' the cold ground. My brother shall know of it, and
    so I thank you for your good counsel. Come, my   70
    coach! Good night, ladies; good night, sweet ladies;
    good night, good night.   [*Exit.*]
King: Follow her close; give her good watch, I pray you.
                           [*Exit Horatio.*]
    O, this is the poison of deep grief; it springs
    All from her father's death. O Gertrude, Gertrude,   75
    When sorrows come, they come not single spies,
    But in battalias! First, her father slain;
    Next, your son gone; and he most violent author
    Of his own just remove; the people muddied,
    Thick and unwholesome in their thoughts and whispers,   80
    For good Polonius' death; and we have done but greenly,
    In hugger-mugger to inter him; poor Ophelia,
    Divided from herself and her fair judgment,
    Without the which we are pictures, or mere beasts:
    Last, and as much containing as all these,   85
    Her brother is in secret come from France,
    Feeds on his wonder, keeps himself in clouds,
    And wants not buzzers to infect his ear
    With pestilent speeches of his father's death;
    Wherein necessity, of matter beggar'd,   90
    Will nothing stick our person to arraign
    In ear and ear. O my dear Gertrude, this,
    Like to a murdering-piece, in many places
    Gives me superfluous death.   [*A noise without.*]
Queen: Alack! what noise is this?
King: Where are my Switzers? Let them guard the door.   95

    [*Enter a Gentleman.*]

97-100 *The ocean . . . officers:* The rebellious people, under
        Laertes' leadership, overwhelm your guards just as an over-
        flowing ocean floods the land.

99   *head:* armed force

101   *as:* as if

102-103 *Antiquity forgot . . . word:* History and established order,
        which are the sources of authority, have been forgotten.

108   *counter:* The image is of hounds following the wrong scent,
        i.e., wrongly accusing Claudius.

116   *cuckold:* a man whose wife has betrayed him; *brands the
        harlot:* burns a mark onto the forehead of a prostitute

117   *unsmirch'd:* unstained, pure

120   *fear our person:* fear for my safety

121   *There's such . . . king:* This is a reference to a belief in the
        divine right of kings, which held that God would establish
        and protect the monarch.

122-123 *That treason . . . will:* Treason cannot accomplish its aims.

What is the matter?

Gentleman: Save yourself, my lord:
   The ocean, overpeering of his list,
   Eats not the flats with more impetuous haste
   Than young Laertes, in a riotous head,
   O'erbears your officers. The rabble call him lord;   100
   And, as the world were now but to begin,
   Antiquity forgot, custom not known,
   The ratifiers and props of every word,
   They cry, "Choose we! Laertes shall be king!"
   Caps, hands and tongues applaud it to the clouds,   105
   "Laertes shall be king, Laertes king!"

Queen: How cheerfully on the false trail they cry!
   O, this is counter, you false Danish dogs!

King: The doors are broke.   [*Noise within.*]

[*Enter Laertes, armed; Danes following.*]

Laertes: Where is this king? Sirs, stand you all without.   110

Danes: No, let's come in.

Laertes: I pray you, give me leave.

Danes: We will, we will.   [*They retire without the door.*]

Laertes: I thank you: keep the door. O thou vile king,
   Give me my father!

Queen: Calmly, good Laertes.

Laertes: That drop of blood that's calm proclaims me bastard, 115
   Cries cuckold to my father, brands the harlot
   Even here, between the chaste unsmirch'd brows
   Of my true mother.

King: What is the cause, Laertes,
   That thy rebellion looks so giant-like?
   Let him go, Gertrude; do not fear our person: 120
   There's such divinity doth hedge a king,
   That treason can but peep to what it would,
   Acts little of his will. Tell me, Laertes,
   Why thou art thus incensed. Let him go, Gertrude:
   Speak man.   125

Laertes: Where is my father?

King: Dead.

Queen: But not by him.

King: Let him demand his fill.

128-134   Laertes is ready to take revenge at any cost.

130   *grace:* divine forgiveness

133   *both the worlds:* i.e., this world and the next; *I give to negligence:* I care nothing about

136   *husband:* manage

139-141   *is't writ . . . loser?:* Is it your intention to destroy both friends and enemies?; *swoopstake:* sweepstake, a game in which "winner takes all"

144   *pelican:* From the way she feeds her offspring, the pelican appears to be letting them eat her flesh; therefore, the pelican was a symbol of self-sacrifice.

145   *Repast:* feed

148   *sensibly:* feeling

149   *level:* directly

152-153   *O heat . . . eye!:* Laertes wishes he could lose his reason (brain) and eyesight.

154-155   *thy madness . . . beam:* The revenge I take on those who caused your madness will be so heavy it will tilt the scale of justice.

158   *mortal:* vulnerable, easily killed

159-161   *Nature is fine . . . loves:* Ophelia's love for her father was so strong that she has sent part of herself—her sanity—with him to the grave.

Laertes: How came he dead? I'll not be juggled with;
    To hell, allegiance! vows, to the blackest devil!
    Conscience and grace, to the profoundest pit!   130
    I dare damnation: to this point I stand,
    That both the worlds I give to negligence,
    Let come what comes; only I'll be revenged
    Most thoroughly for my father.
King: Who shall stay you?
Laertes: My will, not all the world: 135
    And for my means, I'll husband them so well,
    They shall go far with little.
King: Good Laertes.
    If you desire to know the certainty
    Of your dear father's death, is't writ in your revenge
    That, swoopstake, you will draw both friend and foe,   140
    Winner and loser?
Laertes: None but his enemies.
King: Will you know them then?
Laertes: To his good friends thus wide I'll ope my arms;
    And, like the kind life-rendering pelican,
    Repast them with my blood.
King: Why, now you speak   145
    Like a good child and a true gentleman.
    That I am guiltless of your father's death,
    And am most sensibly in grief for it,
    It shall as level to your judgment pierce
    As day does to your eye.
Danes [*Within*]:   Let her come in.   150
Laertes: How now! what noise is that?

    [*Re-enter Ophelia, fantastically dressed with straws and
    flowers.*]

    O heat, dry up my brains! tears seven times salt,
    Burn out the sense and virtue of mine eye!
    By heaven, thy madness shall be paid by weight,
    Till our scale turns the beam. O rose of May!   155
    Dear maid, kind sister, sweet Ophelia!
    O heavens! is't possible a young maid's wits
    Should be as mortal as an old man's life?
    Nature is fine in love, and where 'tis fine

172	*This nothing's more than matter:* This nonsense has more meaning than rational speech does.
173-182	Each of the flowers Ophelia mentions has symbolic meaning. Considering their symbolism, who might receive each one.
174	*pansies:* from the French word "pensées." Pansies are a symbol of thoughts of love.
176	*document:* lesson
178	*fennel:* symbol of flattery; *columbines:* symbol of infidelity in marriage
179	*rue:* symbol of repentance
180	*herb-grace:* herb of repentance
181	*with a difference:* with a different meaning; *daisy:* symbol of false promises of love
182	*violets:* symbol of faithfulness
193	*flaxen:* yellowish-brown (like flax); *poll:* part of the head on which hair grows

It sends some precious instance of itself   160
After the thing it loves.

Ophelia [*Sings*]:   They bore him barefaced on the bier;
                            Hey non nonny, nonny, hey nonny;
                            And on his grave rains many a tear,—

Fare you well, my dove!   165
Laertes: Hadst thou thy wits, and didst persuade revenge,
     It could not move thus.
Ophelia [*Sings*]:   You must sing down-a-down
                            An you call him a-down-a.
     O, how the wheel becomes it! It is the false steward,   170
     that stole his master's daughter.
Laertes: This nothing's more than matter.
Ophelia: There's rosemary, that's for remembrance, pray,
     love, remember: and there is pansies, that's for
     thoughts.   175
Laertes: A document in madness; thoughts and remembrance
     fitted.
Ophelia: There's fennel for you, and columbines: there's
     rue for you; and here's some for me: we may call it
     herb-grace o' Sundays: O, you must wear your rue   180
     with a difference. There's a daisy: I would give you
     some violets, but they withered all when my father died:
     they say he made a good end,—

     [*Sings*]:   For bonny sweet Robin is all my joy.

Laertes: Thought and affliction, passion, hell itself,   185
     She turns to favour and to prettiness.

Ophelia [*Sings*]:   And will a'not come again?
                            And will a'not come again?
                                 No, no, he is dead,
                                 Go to thy death-bed,   190
                            He never will come again.

                            His beard as white as snow,
                            All flaxen was his poll:
                                 He is gone, he is gone,
                                 And we cast away moan: 195
                            God ha' mercy on his soul!

199   *commune with:* share

203   *collateral:* indirect
204   *They find us touch'd:* they find me guilty

210   *obscure:* lowly, degrading
211   *hatchment:* a stone tablet displaying the coat of arms of the
        dead person
212   *formal ostentation:* official ceremony
214   *call't in question:* find an explanation

215   *the great axe:* the executioner's axe

And of all Christian souls, I pray God. God be wi' you!
                                        [*Exit Ophelia.*]
Laertes: Do you see this, O God?
King: Laertes, I must commune with your grief
  Or you deny me right. Go but apart,   200
  Make choice of whom your wisest friends you will,
  And they shall hear and judge 'twixt you and me:
  If by direct or by collateral hand
  They find us touch'd, we will our kingdom give,
  Our crown, our life, and all that we call ours,   205
  To you in satisfaction; but if not,
  Be you content to lend your patience to us,
  And we shall jointly labour with your soul
  To give it due content.
Laertes: Let this be so;
  His means of death, his obscure burial,   210
  No trophy, sword, nor hatchment o'er his bones,
  No noble rite, nor formal ostentation,
  Cry to be heard, as 'twere from heaven to earth,
  That I must call't in question.
King: So you shall;
  And where the offence is let the great axe fall.   215
  I pray you, go with me.   [*Exeunt.*]

Act 4, Scene 5: Activities

1. In the role of Queen Gertrude, write a diary entry in which you reflect on the events in this scene. Among your reflections, include your true feelings about Ophelia's madness, and your feelings toward Claudius and Laertes. Do you think you will be able to keep your promise to Hamlet for much longer?

2. In lines 7–15, Horatio suggests that people will draw dangerous conclusions from Ophelia's incoherent words. With a partner, create a "gossipy" conversation between two court attendants in which they speculate about the meaning behind Ophelia's words. Read some of these conversations aloud to the class.

3. The part of the mad Ophelia is considered to be a very demanding one for both the director and the actress. In groups of five, take the roles of director, costume designer, composer or music director, choreographer, and the actress who plays Ophelia. Conduct a brainstorming session and then report to the class how this scene would be performed. If you prefer, you could design a modern production of the scene.

4. Laertes describes Ophelia's behaviour as a "document in madness" (line 176). In the role of a court psychiatrist, write a commentary about Ophelia's behaviour. Document the behaviour first before commenting on it. You may want to make some comparisons with Hamlet's "antic disposition."

5. Create a dialogue between Claudius and an adviser friend after the events of this scene. In the dialogue, have Claudius reflect about the way in which he handled Laertes. The adviser could make observations about Claudius' actions. Role-play the dialogue for the others.

6. In your group, discuss what hidden meanings and messages might lie behind Ophelia's words, her songs, and her choice of flowers in lines 150–197. Then choose photographs from newspapers, CD covers, or advertising

that might further reveal Ophelia's hidden meanings. Create a scrapbook of these images. Share your group's scrapbook with the class and answer your classmates' questions about your image choices.

7. In groups, choose a segment of this scene to produce as a video that reveals the emotional state of a character. As you plan your production, consider the following:

   • What is the main emotion of the central character?

   • How is that emotion expressed? (Consider both speech and body language.)

   • How are the other characters responding to the emotional state of the central character?

   Rehearse the scene segment, and then prepare a video script. As you plan each shot, try to think of ways of conveying the emotional emphases of the scene. Remember that different camera angles will create different moods. As well, light and colour can alter moods and convey particular feelings. Changing the distance between the camera and the subject will change the focus and balance of a shot.

   As you prepare your shooting script, keep in mind that the audio portion is as important as the video portion. Plan sound effects to support your visual images. Silence can be very effective in conveying emotion as well. Consider music to lead into and out of the scene, and possibly, as background. Share your finished video with the rest of the class.

For the next scene . . .

In your journal, write about a time when, under pressure, you acted in a way that surprised you. What were the consequences? Looking back, how do you feel about your behaviour?

Act 4, Scene 6

In this scene . . .

Sailors have brought letters from Hamlet to Horatio and the King. From the letter to Horatio we learn that Hamlet has escaped from the ship bound for England, and has returned to Denmark. Rosencrantz and Guildenstern have continued the voyage to England.

9	*the ambassador:* i.e., Hamlet
12	*overlooked this:* looked this over
12-30	Notice the condensed, restrained style of Hamlet's letter.
13	*means:* access
15	*appointment:* equipment
17	*compelled valour:* courage that was forced on us by the situation
20	*thieves of mercy:* merciful thieves
22	*repair:* come
25-26	*yet are . . . matter:* My words cannot convey the importance of the event. Hamlet is comparing his words to ammunition that is too small for the gun barrel (bore).

Scene 6

Another room in the castle.
Enter Horatio and a Servant.

Horatio: What are they that would speak with me?
Servant: Sea-faring men, sir; they say they have letters for
    you.
Horatio: Let them come in.   *[Exit Servant.]*
  I do not know from what part of the world
  I should be greeted, if not from lord Hamlet.   5

[Enter Sailors.]

First Sailor: God bless you, sir.
Horatio: Let him bless thee too.
First Sailor: He shall, sir, an't please him. There's a letter
    for you, sir; it comes from the ambassador that was
    bound for England; if your name be Horatio, as I am   10
    let to know it is.
Horatio [Reads]: Horatio, when thou shalt have overlooked
    this, give these fellows some means to the king; they
    have letters for him. Ere we were two days old at
    sea, a pirate of very warlike appointment gave us   15
    chase. Finding ourselves too slow of sail, we put on
    a compelled valour, and in the grapple I boarded
    them: on the instant, they got clear of our ship; so I
    alone became their prisoner. They have dealt with
    me like thieves of mercy; but they knew what they   20
    did; I am to do a good turn for them. Let the king
    have the letters I have sent; and repair thou to me
    with as much speed as thou woulds't fly death. I
    have words to speak in thine ear will make thee
    dumb: yet are they much too light for the bore of   25

31   *way for:* a way to deliver

the matter. These good fellows will bring thee
where I am. Rosencrantz and Guildenstern hold their
course for England: of them I have much to tell
thee. Farewell.
He that thou knowest thine.—*Hamlet.*   30

Come, I will give you way for these your letters;
And do't the speedier, that you may direct me
    To him from whom you brought them.

                                        [*Exeunt.*]

Act 4, Scene 6: Activities

1. Hamlet's short letter leaves many questions unanswered. If you were Horatio, what questions would you want to ask Hamlet?

2. In the role of Horatio, write a letter to a friend at the university in Germany who also knows Hamlet. Tell the friend about the content and tone of Hamlet's letter. Give your reflections on how Hamlet may have changed since he was banished from Elsinore.

3. Since we do not yet know the contents of Hamlet's letter to Claudius, compose a 20-word message Hamlet might have sent to him. You might consider such things as announcing your return, and hinting about what you have discovered about Claudius' schemes. Read the message to your group. Then together, discuss the implications of each group member's message.

For the next scene . . .

In your journal, write about a time when someone used flattery to manipulate you into doing something. Have you ever tried to manipulate someone else through flattery? What were the results?

Act 4, Scene 7

In this scene . . .

This scene introduces a strong counterplot against Hamlet. It begins with Claudius convincing Laertes that Hamlet was responsible for Polonius' murder. The letter from Hamlet is delivered, announcing his return to Denmark. Claudius manipulates Laertes into a plan to kill Hamlet in a duelling match. Laertes adds to the plan by offering to put a deadly poison on the end of his sword. Claudius suggests a cup of poisoned wine for Hamlet, if the first plan fails. The conversation is interrupted by Gertrude, who announces that Ophelia is dead.

1	*Now must . . . seal:* Now that you know the facts, you will confirm my innocence.
3	*Sith:* since
6	*feats:* actions
7	*capital:* punishable by death
9	*mainly:* very greatly
10	*unsinew'd:* weak
13	*be it either which:* whichever of the two it might be
14	*conjunctive:* closely linked
17	*count:* trial
18	*general gender:* common people
21	*Convert his gyves to graces:* change his fetters to adornments, i.e., make a martyr of him
21-24	*so that my arrows . . . aim'd them:* The public's affection for Hamlet is so strong that my plan for dealing with him would be turned against me, just as an arrow that is too light would be turned back by a strong wind, missing its mark.
26	*terms:* circumstances
27	*go back again:* refer to her as she used to be
28	*Stood challenger . . . age:* was unequalled in her time

Scene 7

Another room in the castle.
Enter King and Laertes.

King: Now must your conscience my acquittance seal.
  And you must put me in your heart for friend,
  Sith you have heard, and with a knowing ear,
  That he which hath your noble father slain,
  Pursued my life.
Laertes:　　　　　　It well appears: but tell me   5
  Why you proceeded not against these feats,
  So crimeful and so capital in nature,
  As by your safety, wisdom, all things else,
  You mainly were stirr'd up.
King:　　　　　　　　O, for two special reasons,
  Which may to you perhaps seem much unsinew'd,   10
  And yet to me they're strong. The queen his mother
  Lives almost by his looks; and for myself—
  My virtue or my plague, be it either which—
  She's so conjunctive to my life and soul,
  That, as the star moves not but in his sphere,   15
  I could not but by her. The other motive,
  Why to a public count I might not go,
  Is the great love the general gender bear him;
  Who, dipping all his faults in their affection,
  Would, like the spring that turneth wood to stone,   20
  Convert his gyves to graces; so that my arrows,
  Too slightly timber'd for so loud a wind,
  Would have reverted to my bow again
  And not where I had aim'd them.
Laertes: And so have I a noble father lost;   25
  A sister driven into desperate terms,
  Whose worth, if praises may go back again,
  Stood challenger on mount of all the age
  For her perfections: but my revenge will come.

33   *You shortly shall hear more:* Claudius is expecting news of Hamlet's death in England.

50   *abuse:* deception

52   *character:* handwriting

59   *it:* i.e., Hamlet's return

63   *checking at:* turning back from. The image is taken from falconry. Sometimes the hawk would swerve away from (check at) its prey to chase some other bird.

King: Break not your sleeps for that: you must not think   30
    That we are made of stuff so flat and dull
    That we can let our beard be shook with danger
    And think it pastime. You shortly shall hear more:
    I loved your father, and we love ourself;
    And that, I hope, will teach you to imagine—   35

[Enter a Messenger with letters.]

    How now! what news?
Messenger: Letters, my lord, from Hamlet:
    This to your majesty; this to the queen.
King: From Hamlet! Who brought them?
Messenger: Sailors, my lord, they say: I saw them not:
    They were given to me by Claudio; he received them   40
    Of him that brought them.
King: Laertes, you shall hear them.
    Leave us.   *[Exit Messenger.]*
    [Reads]: High and mighty, You shall know, I am set
      naked on your kingdom. To-morrow shall I beg leave   45
      to see your kingly eyes: when I shall, first asking
      your pardon thereunto, recount the occasions of my
      sudden and more strange return.—*Hamlet.*
    What should this mean? Are all the rest come back?
    Or is it some abuse, and no such thing?   50
Laertes: Know you the hand?
King: 'Tis Hamlet's character. "Naked!"
    And in a postscript here, he says "alone."
    Can you advise me?
Laertes: I am lost in it, my lord. But let him come: 55
    It warms the very sickness in my heart,
    That I shall live and tell him to his teeth,
    "Thus diddest thou!"
King: If it be so, Laertes,—
    As how should it be so? how otherwise?—
    Will you be ruled by me?
Laertes: Ay, my lord;   60
    If so you'll not o'errule me to a peace.
King: To thine own peace. If he be now return'd,
    As checking at his voyage, and that he means
    No more to undertake it, I will work him

65	*device:* contrivance, plotting
68	*uncharge the practice:* not accuse us
71	*organ:* instrument (for killing Hamlet)
74	*your sum of parts:* all your qualities
77	*unworthiest siege:* least worth
78	*riband:* ribbon
80, 81	*livery, weeds:* clothing
85	*can:* are skillful
88-89	*As he . . . beast:* as if he and the horse were one being (like the centaurs of classical mythology)
89-91	*so far . . . did:* His actions surpassed anything I expected or could even imagine.
94	*brooch:* main ornament
96	*made confession of you:* acknowledged your skill
97	*masterly report:* report of your mastery
98	*defence:* fencing (means of defence)
99	*rapier:* a two-edged sword, popular in fencing

To an exploit now ripe in my device,   65
Under the which he shall not choose but fall,
And for his death no wind of blame shall breathe;
But even his mother shall uncharge the practice,
And call it accident.
Laertes: My lord, I will be ruled:
    The rather, if you could devise it so   70
    That I might be the organ.
King: It falls right.
    You have been talk'd of since your travel much,
    And that in Hamlet's hearing, for a quality
    Wherein, they say, you shine: your sum of parts
    Did not together pluck such envy from him,   75
    As did that one, and that, in my regard,
    Of the unworthiest siege.
Laertes: What part is that, my lord?
King: A very riband in the cap of youth,
    Yet needful too; for youth no less becomes
    The light and careless livery that it wears   80
    Than settled age his sables and his weeds,
    Importing health and graveness. Two months since
    Here was a gentleman of Normandy:—
    I've seen myself, and served against, the French,
    And they can well on horseback: but this gallant   85
    Had witchcraft in't; he grew into his seat,
    And to such wondrous doing brought his horse
    As he had been incorpsed and demi-natured
    With the brave beast: so far he topp'd my thought
    That I, in forgery of shapes and tricks   90
    Come short of what he did.
Laertes: A Norman was't?
King: A Norman.
Laertes: Upon my life, Lamond.
King: The very same.
Laertes: I know him well: he is the brooch indeed
    And gem of all the nation.   95
King: He made confession of you,
    And gave you such a masterly report,
    For art and exercise in your defence,
    And for your rapier most especial,

101   *scrimers:* fencers

102   *motion:* the movements that fencers are trained in

106   *play:* to engage in a fencing match

112-114 *love is . . . it:* Time brings love into being and also causes it to die.

115-116 *There lives . . . abate it:* The snuff is the charred wick of a candle which causes the flame to dim. The idea is that love carries within it the cause of its own destruction.

117   *And nothing . . . still:* Nothing remains at the same level of goodness forever.

118   *plurisy:* excess

118-124 Ironically, Claudius is commenting on the weaknesses in Hamlet that have prevented him from killing Claudius.

121   *abatements:* a lessening in intensity

123   *spendthrift sigh:* It was believed that each sigh drew blood from the heart. A sigh gave temporary relief, but it harmed the person by carelessly wasting lifeblood.

124   *the quick o' the ulcer:* the heart of the trouble

128   *sanctuarize:* provide safety, refuge. In mediaeval times, murderers could seek sanctuary in a church.

132   *put on:* appoint

134   *in fine:* finally

135   *remiss:* carelessly trustful

That he cried out, 'twould be a sight indeed   100
If one could match you: the scrimers of their nation,
He swore, had neither motion, guard, nor eye,
If you opposed them. Sir, this report of his
Did Hamlet so envenom with his envy
That he could nothing do but wish and beg   105
Your sudden coming o'er, to play with him.
Now, out of this,——
Laertes: What out of this, my lord?
King: Laertes, was your father dear to you?
  Or are you like the painting of a sorrow,
  A face without a heart?
Laertes: Why ask you this?   110
King: Not that I think you did not love your father,
  But that I know love is begun by time,
  And that I see, in passages of proof,
  Time qualifies the spark and fire of it.
  There lives within the very flame of love   115
  A kind of wick or snuff that will abate it;
  And nothing is at a like goodness still,
  For goodness, growing to a plurisy,
  Dies in his own too-much: that we would do
  We should do when we would; for this "would" changes   120
  And hath abatements and delays as many
  As there are tongues, are hands, are accidents,
  And then this "should" is like a spendthrift sigh,
  That hurts by easing. But, to the quick o' the ulcer:
  Hamlet comes back: what would you undertake,   125
  To show yourself your father's son in deed
  More than in words?
Laertes: To cut his throat i' the church.
King: No place indeed should murder sanctuarize;
  Revenge should have no bounds. But, good Laertes,
  Will you do this, keep close within your chamber.   130
  Hamlet return'd shall know you are come home:
  We'll put on those shall praise your excellence
  And set a double varnish on the fame
  The Frenchman gave you; bring you in fine together
  And wager on your heads: he, being remiss,   135
  Most generous, and free from all contriving,

137   *peruse:* examine

139   *unabated:* unprotected, with the point exposed; *pass of practice:* practice round, or well-rehearsed (treacherous) thrust

140   *Requite:* repay

142   *unction:* ointment; *mountebank:* a travelling quack doctor

143   *mortal:* deadly

144   *cataplasm:* poultice, bandage

145   *simples:* medicinal herbs; *virtue:* power

146   *Under the moon:* Herbs collected by moonlight were thought to be especially powerful.

148   *contagion:* poison; *gall:* graze his skin

150-151   *Weigh . . . shape:* Consider the best time and action to achieve our purpose.

152-153   *And that . . . assay'd:* If our scheme becomes obvious because we didn't carry it out well, it would be better not to attempt it at all.

154   *back:* backup plan

155   *blast in proof:* fail (be destroyed in the attempt)

156   *your cunnings:* your respective skills

161   *chalice:* a wine goblet; *nonce:* occasion

162   *stuck:* sword thrust

168   *willow:* The willow tree is a symbol of lost love.

169   *hoar:* The underside of a willow leaf is white like frost (hoar).

172   *liberal:* free of speech; here, lewd

Will not peruse the foils, so that with ease,
Or with a little shuffling, you may choose
A sword unbated, and, in a pass of practice
Requite him for your father.
Laertes: I will do't: 140
And for that purpose I'll anoint my sword.
I bought an unction of a mountebank,
So mortal, that but dip a knife in it,
Where it draws blood no cataplasm so rare,
Collected from all simples that have virtue   145
Under the moon, can save the thing from death
That is but scratch'd withal: I'll touch my point
With this contagion, that, if I gall him slightly,
It may be death.
King: Let's further think of this;
Weigh what convenience both of time and means   150
May fit us to our shape: if this should fail,
And that our drift look through our bad performance,
'Twere better not assay'd; therefore this project
Should have a back or second, that might hold
If this should blast in proof. Soft!—let me see: 155
We'll make a solemn wager on your cunnings:
I ha't!
When in your motion you are hot and dry—
As make your bouts more violent to that end—
And that he calls for drink, I'll have prepared him   160
A chalice for the nonce; whereon but sipping,
If he by chance escape your venom'd stuck,
Our purpose may hold there. But stay, what noise?

[Enter Queen.]

How now, sweet queen?
Queen: One woe doth tread upon another's heel,   165
So fast they follow: your sister's drown'd, Laertes.
Laertes: Drown'd! O, where?
Queen: There is a willow grows aslant a brook,
That shows his hoar leaves in the glassy stream;
There, with fantastic garlands did she come   170
Of crow-flowers, nettles, daisies, and long purples,
That liberal shepherds give a grosser name,

173 *cold:* chaste

174 *pendent:* overhanging; *coronet weeds:* flowers woven into a crown

175 *envious:* spiteful; *sliver:* small branch

180 *incapable:* unaware

181-182 *a creature . . . element:* a creature that lives in water

189 *trick:* human nature

191 *The woman will be out:* These tears will be the last signs of womanly behaviour in me.

193 *doubts:* extinguishes

But our cold maids do dead-men's-fingers call them;
There, on the pendent boughs her coronet weeds
Clambering to hang, an envious sliver broke;   175
When down the weedy trophies and herself
Fell in the weeping brook. Her clothes spread wide,
And mermaid-like a while they bore her up:
Which time she chanted snatches of old tunes,
As one incapable of her own distress,   180
Or like a creature native and indued
Unto that element: but long it could not be,
Till that her garments, heavy with their drink,
Pull'd the poor wretch from her melodious lay
To muddy death.
Laertes: Alas! then, she is drown'd!   185
Queen: Drown'd, drown'd.
Laertes: Too much of water hast thou, poor Ophelia,
And therefore I forbid my tears: but yet
It is our trick; nature her custom holds,
Let shame say what it will: when these are gone,   190
The woman will be out. Adieu, my lord:
I have a speech of fire that fain would blaze,
But that this folly doubts it.   [*Exit.*]
King: Let's follow, Gertrude:
How much I had to do to calm his rage!
Now fear I this will give it start again;   195
Therefore let's follow.   [*Exeunt.*]

Act 4, Scene 7: Activities

1. Claudius singles out the words "naked and alone" from Hamlet's letter. Discuss with the class what these words might mean to Claudius. Suggest other phrases in the letter that might worry him.

2. Choose two or three parts in Claudius' conversation with Laertes where you will insert Claudius' private thoughts while he is speaking these words. Have a partner speak the words from the text and pause in appropriate spots, so that you can vocalize Claudius' inner thoughts. Present some of these adaptations to the class.

3. List the thoughts or images that could be flashing through Gertrude's mind as she tells Laertes and Claudius about Ophelia's death. If you were filming this scene, would you show these images as Gertrude is talking?

4. As a reporter for a nightly television newscast, you have been sent with a camera crew to do a two-minute report on the death of Ophelia. What backdrop setting would you use to deliver your report? Whom would you try to interview? What else would you try to film? Would you emphasize the individual human loss or the political situation? Prepare the script of the news report, including directions for the camera and the text of the interview.

5. Do you think Ophelia's death should be considered suicide? What effect did the details of her death create on you? What effect do you think Shakespeare wanted to create? Was Ophelia an innocent victim? Discuss your ideas in groups.

Act 4: Consider the Whole Act

1. Make your own predictions about events that you will witness in the next Act:

   - How will Hamlet behave when he returns to the castle?
   - How will he react to the news of Ophelia's death?
   - How will he deal with Laertes?

   Add other predictions about future events. Share your predictions with your group, and explain why you think these events will happen.

2. Earlier in the play, Hamlet said, "Frailty, thy name is woman!" (I, ii, 146). Considering the behaviour of Gertrude and Ophelia in Act 4, would you support or refute Hamlet's assessment of women? In your group, prepare notes for a debate on the topic. Using these notes, you could go on to conduct a formal debate.

3. Although Claudius is clearly an unscrupulous character, he has some qualities that could be considered admirable. Make a list of his admirable qualities, with references as to where in Act 4 they are best demonstrated.

4. After considering how you respond to Claudius' character, think about villains or antagonists in contemporary popular culture (consider novels, movies, and television). What seems to motivate them? Why are we interested in them? Interview a range of people on this subject, and then write an essay or make a presentation to the class about villains in modern media.

5. Think about Hamlet's definition of greatness:

   > . . . Rightly to be great
   > Is not to stir without great argument,
   > But greatly to find quarrel in a straw
   > When honour's at the stake . . .
   > (IV, iv, 52–55)

   With Hamlet's idea in mind, consider a recent newsworthy event in which someone took a strong stand because honour was at stake. (You will have to define "honour.") Do you agree with the stand that was taken? Write an editorial about this event, using some of Hamlet's words and / or ideas.

6. Hamlet, Laertes, and Fortinbras are three very different young men, but they are all involved in conflicts in which their honour is at stake. Divide a page in three columns vertically, one column for each character. Then divide the page horizontally using the following headings:

   - The Problem
   - The Plan of Action
   - The Help He Has

   Once you have filled in this chart, predict how well each character will carry out his plan. Discuss your predictions in groups or with the class.

7. Write a self-help article for students about procrastination. Offer empathy and good advice about this problem. Use quotations such as Claudius' speech in IV, vii, 119–124, or Hamlet's soliloquy in IV, iv, 31–65.

8. Scenes 1, 2, and 3 of this Act provided an opportunity to see both Claudius and Hamlet under stress. Write an article about how different people react to stress, using Hamlet and Claudius as examples.

9. In a group, plan how you would direct the section of Scene 5 where Ophelia appears for the second time (lines 152–198). On a photocopy of these pages, create director's notes to indicate costuming, stage directions, movements, pauses, type of music, lighting, and other effects. Make a sketch of your set design. Afterward, you may choose to direct this scene for a class performance.

For the next scene . . .

In your journal, write about a time when someone you know had an experience that changed his or her personality or attitude to life. Did you believe that the change was real? What circumstances might cause a person to change greatly in a short period of time?

Act 5, Scene 1

In this scene . . .

Two gravediggers (played by clowns) are preparing Ophelia's grave. As they pass the time joking about their work, Hamlet and Horatio approach and join in their conversation. Hamlet comes upon the skull of Yorick, a court jester who entertained Hamlet in his childhood. Ophelia's funeral procession approaches, and Hamlet learns that Ophelia is dead. When Laertes expresses his grief by leaping into Ophelia's grave, Hamlet also leaps in and fights with him. As the scene ends, Claudius reminds Laertes of their plan to murder Hamlet.

Stage direction

Enter two clowns: The first and second clowns are gravediggers. They are simple, rough people.

1   *Christian burial:* This question arises because suicides were denied Christian funeral rites.

4   *straight:* right away. *The crowner hath sat on her:* The coroner has considered her case; *finds:* has given a verdict

9   *"se offendendo":* a mistaken attempt at the legal term "se defendendo" (in self-defence)

9-13   The gravedigger creates humour by confusing legal terminology and by attempting to construct a legal argument.

12   *argal:* a corruption of "ergo" (therefore)

17   *will he, nill he:* willy-nilly, i.e., willingly or not

22   *marry:* indeed; *crowner's quest law:* coroner's inquest law

25   *out o' Christian burial:* without Christian ceremony

26   *there thou say'st:* that's right

27   *countenance:* permission

28-29   *even Christian:* fellow Christians. *Come, my spade:* Hand me my spade.

31   *hold up:* follow

Act 5, Scene 1

A churchyard.
Enter two Clowns, with
spades, etc.

First Clown: Is she to be buried in Christian burial that
    wilfully seeks her own salvation?
Second Clown: I tell thee she is; and therefore make her
    grave straight: the crowner hath sat on her, and finds
    it Christian burial.   5
First Clown: How can that be, unless she drowned herself
    in her own defence?
Second Clown: Why, 'tis found so.
First Clown: It must be "se offendendo"; it cannot be else.
    For here lies the point: if I drown myself wittingly,   10
    it argues an act: and an act hath three branches; it is,
    to act, to do, and to perform: argal, she drowned
    herself wittingly.
Second Clown: Nay, but hear you, goodman delver.
First Clown: Give me leave. Here lies the water; good: here   15
    stands the man; good: if the man go to this water, and
    drown himself, it is, will he, nill he, he goes; mark
    you that; but if the water come to him and drown him,
    he drowns not himself: argal, he that is not guilty of
    his own death, shortens not his own life.   20
Second Clown: But is this law?
First Clown: Ay, marry is't; crowner's quest law.
Second Clown: Will you ha' the truth on't? If this had not
    been a gentlewoman, she should have been buried
    out o'Christian burial.   25
First Clown: Why, there thou say'st: and the more pity that
    great folk should have countenance in this world to
    drown or hang themselves, more than their even
    Christian. Come, my spade. There is no ancient
    gentlemen but gardeners, ditchers, and gravemakers;   30
    they hold up Adam's profession.

33   *bore arms:* a pun — had arms or had weapons

38-39   *confess thyself:* The rest of this saying was "and be hanged."

40   *Go to:* nonsense

42   *mason:* a worker in stone; *shipwright:* a shipbuilder

52   *unyoke:* take a rest (as when oxen were unyoked)

55   *Mass:* by the Mass

60   *Yaughan:* Possibly Yaughan was a tavern-keeper near the Globe Theatre; *stoup:* large drinking cup

Second Clown: Was he a gentleman?
First Clown: A' was the first that ever bore arms.
Second Clown: Why, he had none.
First Clown: What, art a heathen? How dost thou understand   35
    the Scripture? The Scripture says, Adam digged: could
    he dig without arms? I'll put another question to thee:
    if thou answerest me not to the purpose, confess
    thyself—
Second Clown: Go to.   40
First Clown: What is he, that builds stronger than either
    the mason, the shipwright, or the carpenter?
Second Clown: The gallows-maker; for that frame outlives
    a thousand tenants.
First Clown: I like thy wit well, in good faith; the gallows   45
    does well: but how does it well? it does well to those
    that do ill: now, thou dost ill to say the gallows is built
    stronger than the church; argal, the gallows may do
    well to thee. To't again; come.
Second Clown: Who builds stronger than a mason, a   50
    shipwright, or a carpenter?
First Clown: Ay, tell me that, and unyoke.
Second Clown: Marry, now I can tell.
First Clown: To't.
Second Clown: Mass, I cannot tell.   55

   [Enter Hamlet and Horatio at a distance.]

First Clown: Cudgel thy brains no more about it, for your
    dull ass will not mend his pace with beating, and
    when you are asked this question next, say "a grave-
    maker": the houses that he makes last till doomsday.
    Go, get thee to Yaughan; fetch me a stoup of liquor.   60
                          [Exit Second Clown.]

  [First Clown digs, and sings.]

  In youth, when I did love, did love,
    Methought it was very sweet,
  To contract, O, the time, for—a my behove,
    O, methought there—a was nothing—a meet.

Hamlet: Hath this fellow no feeling of his business, that he   65
    sings at grave-making!

67-68	*Custom . . . easiness:* Because he is accustomed to this (gruesome) work, he's at ease with it.
69-70	*the hand . . . sense:* The hand that isn't accustomed to work is more sensitive.
73	*intill:* into
76	*jowls:* knocks
77	*Cain's jaw-bone:* Cain is said to have killed his brother Abel with the jaw-bone of an ass.
78	*pate of a politician:* head of a crafty schemer; *o'er-reaches:* gets the better of
79	*circumvent:* outsmart
81	*courtier:* Courtiers were known for flattery.
86	*chapless:* jawless
87	*mazzard:* head; *sexton:* a person who takes care of church property
88	*revolution:* turn of the Wheel of Fortune; *trick:* skill
90	*loggats:* a game in which sticks are thrown at the ground
95-109	Hamlet is pointing out the uselessness of all the fine points of the law, since everything ends in the grave anyway.
96, 97	*quiddities, quillets:* arguments and fine points of the law
97	*tenures:* rights to property
99	*sconce:* head
100	*action of battery:* a pun—the gravedigger's act of banging the skull about the lawyer's charge (legal action) against the gravedigger for assault (battery)

Horatio: Custom hath made it in him a property of
    easiness.
Hamlet: 'Tis e'en so: the hand of little employment hath
    the daintier sense.   70
  First Clown [*Sings*]:

        But age, with his stealing steps,
           Hath claw'd me in his clutch,
      And hath shipped me intill the land,
          As if I had never been such.

                      [Throws up a skull.]

Hamlet: That skull had a tongue in it, and could sing once: 75
    how the knave jowls it to the ground, as if it were
    Cain's jaw-bone, that did the first murder! It might be
    the pate of a politician which this ass now o'er-reaches;
    one that would circumvent God, might it not?
Horatio: It might, my lord   80
Hamlet: Or of a courtier; which could say, "Good-morrow,
    sweet lord! How dost thou, good lord?" This might
    be my lord such-a-one, that praised my lord such-a-one's
    horse, when he meant to beg it, might it not?
Horatio: Ay, my lord.   85
Hamlet: Why, e'en so: and now my lady Worm's: chapless,
    and knocked about the mazzard with a sexton's spade:
    here's a fine revolution, if we had the trick to see't. Did
    these bones cost no more the breeding, but to play
    at loggats with them? mine ache to think on't.   90

   First Clown [*Sings*]:

        A pickaxe, and a spade, a spade,
           For and a shrouding sheet:
      O, a pit of clay for to be made
          For such a guest is meet.

                    [Throws up another
skull.]

Hamlet: There's another! Why might not that be the skull   95
    of a lawyer? Where be his quiddities, now, his
    quillets, his cases, his tenures, and his tricks? why does
    he suffer this rude knave now to knock him about the
    sconce with a dirty shovel, and will not tell him of his
    action of battery? Hum! This fellow might be in's time   100

101,103   *statutes, recoveries:* legal terms to do with land rights

103-109   *is this . . . more:* is the end of all this man's complicated efforts that the land he finally possesses (i.e., his grave) is so small it would hardly hold all his paperwork?

107   *conveyances:* deeds

108   *box:* coffin

119   *liest:* used in a double sense — to reside and to tell a lie

123   *the quick:* the living

124   *quick:* swift (another pun; see line 123)

133   *absolute:* exact with words

133-134   *by the card:* precisely; *equivocation:* ambiguity

135-137   *the age . . . kibe:* Hamlet is commenting on peasants who imitate the manners of courtiers. The image is of one man following another so closely that he chafes (galls) the chilblains (kibe) of the man ahead.

136   *picked:* refined, fussy

a great buyer of land, with his statutes, his
recognizances, his fines, his double vouchers, his
recoveries: is this the fine of his fines and the recovery
of his recoveries, to have his fine pate full of fine dirt?
will his vouchers vouch him no more of his purchases,   105
and double ones too, than the length and breadth of
a pair of indentures? The very conveyances of his
lands will hardly lie in this box, and must the inheritor
himself have no more, ha?

Horatio: Not a jot more, my lord.   110

Hamlet: Is not parchment made of sheep-skins?

Horatio: Ay, my lord, and of calf-skins too.

Hamlet: They are sheep and calves that seek out assurance
in that. I will speak to this fellow. Whose grave's this,
sir?   115

First Clown: Mine, sir.

> [*Sings*]:   O, a pit of clay for to be made
> For such a guest is meet.

Hamlet: I think it be thine, indeed, for thou liest in't.

First Clown: You lie out on't, sir, and therefore 'tis not   120
yours: for my part, I do not lie in't, and yet it is mine.

Hamlet: Thou dost lie in't, to be in't, and say it is thine:
'tis for the dead, not for the quick; therefore thou liest.

First Clown: 'Tis a quick lie, sir; 'twill away again, from
me to you.   125

Hamlet: What man dost thou dig it for?

First Clown: For no man, sir.

Hamlet: What woman, then?

First Clown: For none, neither.

Hamlet: Who is to be buried in't?   130

First Clown: One that was a woman, sir; but, rest her soul,
she's dead.

Hamlet: How absolute the knave is! we must speak by the
card, or equivocation will undo us. By the lord,
Horatio, these three years I have taken note of it: the   135
age is grown so picked that the toe of the peasant
comes so near the heel of the courtier, he galls his kibe.
How long has thou been a grave-maker?

First Clown: Of all the days i' the year, I came to't that

159   *How long . . . rot?:* Notice again Hamlet's preoccupation with death and decay.

160   *pocky:* diseased, infected with the pox

161   *laying in:* burial

170   *whoreson:* a casual expression of contempt

174   *flagon of Rhenish:* bottle of Rhine wine

day that our last king Hamlet o'ercame Fortinbras.   140
Hamlet: How long is that since?
First Clown: Cannot you tell that? every fool can tell that.
　　It was the very day that young Hamlet was born; he
　　that was mad, and sent into England.
Hamlet: Ay, marry, why was he sent into England?   145
First Clown: Why, because a' was mad: a' shall recover his
　　wits there: or, if a' do not, it's no great matter there.
Hamlet: Why?
First Clown: 'Twill not be seen in him there; there the men
　　are as mad as he.   150
Hamlet: How came he mad?
First Clown: Very strangely, they say.
Hamlet: How "strangely"?
First Clown: 'Faith, e'en with losing his wits.
Hamlet: Upon what ground?   155
First Clown: Why, here in Denmark. I have been sexton
　　here, man and boy, thirty years.
Hamlet: How long will a man lie i' the earth ere he rot?
First Clown: 'Faith, if a' be not rotten before a' die—as we
　　have many pocky corses nowadays, that will scarce   160
　　hold the laying in—he will last you some eight year or
　　nine year: a tanner will last you nine year.
Hamlet: Why he more than another?
First Clown: Why, sir his hide is so tanned with his trade,
　　that a' will keep out water a great while; and your   165
　　water is a sore decayer of your dead body. Here's a skull
　　now: this skull has lain in the earth three-and-twenty
　　years.
Hamlet: Whose was it?
First Clown: A whoreson mad fellow's it was: whose do you   170
　　think it was?
Hamlet: Nay, I know not.
First Clown: A pestilence on him for a mad rogue! a' poured
　　a flagon of Rhenish on my head once. This same skull,
　　sir, was Yorick's skull, the King's jester.   175
Hamlet: This?
First Clown: E'en that.
Hamlet: Let me see. [*Takes the skull.*] Alas, poor Yorick! I
　　knew him, Horatio; a fellow of infinite jest, of most

182   *my gorge rises at it:* It turns my stomach. Hamlet is not sickened by the skull itself, but by the fact that it once belonged to someone he knew.

184   *gibes:* jokes; *gambols:* jumping around, dancing

185-186   *that were wont . . . roar:* that used to make the people at the table roar with laughter

187   *chap-fallen:* with a hanging jaw, dejected

188   *paint:* put on makeup; *favour:* appearance

192   *Alexander:* Alexander the Great

199   *bung-hole:* a hole in a barrel

200   *curiously:* minutely, strangely

201-202   *with modesty . . . it:* without exaggeration and following probability

207   *Imperious:* imperial

210   *flaw:* a sudden gust of wind

213   *maimed rites:* shortened (mutilated) ceremony; *betoken:* suggest

215   *Fordo:* destroy; *estate:* rank

excellent fancy: he hath borne me on his back a   180
thousand times; and now how abhorred in my
imagination it is! my gorge rises at it. Here hung those
lips that I have kissed I know not how oft. Where be
your gibes now? your gambols? your songs? your
flashes of merriment, that were wont to set the table   185
on a roar: Not one now, to mock your own grinning?
quite chap-fallen? Now get you to my lady's chamber,
and tell her, let her paint an inch thick, to this favour
she must come; make her laugh at that. Prithee,
Horatio, tell me one thing.   190

Horatio: What's that, my lord?

Hamlet: Dost thou think Alexander looked o' this fashion
   i' the earth?

Horatio: E'en so.

Hamlet: And smelt so? pah!   [*Throws down the skull.*]   195

Horatio: E'en so, my lord.

Hamlet: To what base uses we may return, Horatio!
   Why may not imagination trace the noble dust of
   Alexander, till he find it stopping a bung-hole?

Horatio: 'Twere to consider too curiously, to consider so.   200

Hamlet: No, faith, not a jot; but to follow him thither with
   modesty enough and likelihood to lead it; as thus:
   Alexander died, Alexander was buried, Alexander
   returned into dust; the dust is earth; of earth we make
   loam: and why of that loam, whereto he was converted, 205
   might they not stop a beer-barrel?
      Imperious Cæsar, dead, and turn'd to clay,
      Might stop a hole to keep the wind away:
      O, that that earth which kept the world in awe,
      Should patch a wall to expel the winter's flaw!   210
But soft, but soft! aside: here comes the king.

*[Enter Priests, etc., in procession; the corpse of
Ophelia, Laertes and Mourners following; King, Queen,
their Trains, etc.]*

The queen, the courtiers: who is that they follow?
And with such maimed rites! This doth betoken,
The corse they follow did with desperate hand
Fordo its own life: 'twas of some estate.   215

216	*Couch we:* Let's hide
220-221	*Her obsequies . . . warranty:* She has had as much of a funeral as the authorities permit.
221	*her death was doubtful:* It is not clear whether or not she committed suicide.
222	*great command:* the King's command; *order:* regular church practice
223	*in ground unsanctified:* Suicides could not be buried in a churchyard, i.e., in holy ground.
224	*for:* instead of
225	*Shards:* pieces of broken pottery
226	*virgin crants:* It was customary to hang flower wreaths (crants) in the church at a maiden's funeral.
227	*strewments:* flowers strewn on the grave
227-228	*the bringing home of:* bringing her to her final home with
231	*requiem:* music for the dead
232	*peace-parted souls:* souls who died in peace
234	*churlish:* rude
236	*howling:* i.e., in hell
240-248	Laertes' exaggerated expression of grief, which Hamlet will soon try to match, is called "ranting."
242	*ingenious sense:* lively intelligence
244	*Till I . . . arms:* Ophelia was buried in an open coffin.
247,248	*Pelion, Olympus:* high mountains in Greece. Olympus was the home of the gods.
247	*skyish:* reaching the sky
249	*Bears such an emphasis:* expresses itself with such force

Couch we awhile, and mark.   [*Retiring with Horatio.*]
Laertes: What ceremony else?
Hamlet: That is Laertes, a very noble youth: mark.
Laertes: What ceremony else?
First Priest: Her obsequies have been as far enlarged   220
  As we have warranty: her death was doubtful;
  And, but that great command o'ersways the order,
  She should in ground unsanctified have lodged
  Till the last trumpet; for charitable prayers,
  Shards, flints and pebbles should be thrown on her: 225
  Yet here she is allow'd her virgin crants,
  Her maiden strewments and the bringing home
  Of bell and burial.
Laertes: Must there no more be done?
First Priest: No more be done!
  We should profane the service of the dead,   230
  To sing a requiem and such rest to her
  As to peace-parted souls.
Laertes: Lay her i' the earth;
  And from her fair and unpolluted flesh
  May violets spring! I tell thee, churlish priest,
  A minist'ring angel shall my sister be,   235
  When thou liest howling.
Hamlet: What, the fair Ophelia!
Queen [*Scattering flowers*]: Sweets to the sweet: fare well!
  I hoped thou shouldst have been my Hamlet's wife;
  I thought thy bride-bed to have deck'd, sweet maid,
  And not t' have strew'd thy grave.
Laertes: O, treble woe   240
  Fall ten times treble on that cursed head
  Whose wicked deed thy most ingenious sense
  Deprived thee of! Hold off the earth a while,
  Till I have caught her once more in mine arms:
                    [*Leaps into the grave.*]
  Now pile your dust upon the quick and dead,   245
  Till of this flat a mountain you have made
  To o'ertop old Pelion or the skyish head
  Of blue Olympus.
Hamlet [*Advancing*]: What is he whose grief
  Bears such an emphasis? whose phrase of sorrow

250	*Conjures the wandering stars:* charms the planets. The planets change their position in relation to the stars and were thought of, therefore, as "wandering."
251	*wonder-wounded:* struck by astonishment
255	*splenitive:* hot-headed. The spleen was considered the source of rage in the body.
261	*wag:* move
267	*forbear him:* leave him alone
269	*woul't:* wilt thou; *tear thyself:* rend your clothing
270	*eisel:* vinegar
272	*outface:* outdo
273	*quick:* alive
274-277	*And, if . . . wart!:* Hamlet is outdoing Laertes' references to mountains (247–248) by saying that Ossa, another Greek mountain, will look as small as a wart in comparison to the "millions of acres" of earth they will be buried under.
276	*Singeing . . . zone:* burning its head in the sun's region
277	*an thou'lt mouth:* if you rant
278	*mere:* complete, utter
280	*Anon:* soon
281	*When . . . are disclosed:* when her (the dove's) two fledglings, covered with yellow down, are hatched

Conjures the wandering stars, and makes them stand   250
Like wonder-wounded hearers? This is I,
Hamlet the Dane!   [*Leaps into the grave.*]
Laertes: The devil take thy soul!   [*Grappling with him.*]
Hamlet: Thou pray'st not well.
  I prithee, take thy fingers from my throat;
  For, though I am not splenitive and rash,   255
  Yet have I something in me dangerous,
  Which let thy wisdom fear. Hold off thy hand!
King: Pluck them asunder.
Queen: Hamlet, Hamlet!
All: Gentlemen,—
Horatio: Good my lord, be quiet.
  [*The Attendants part them, and they come out of the grave.*]
Hamlet: Why, I will fight with him upon this theme   260
  Until my eyelids will no longer wag.
Queen: O my son, what theme?
Hamlet: I loved Ophelia; forty thousand brothers
  Could not, with all their quantity of love,
  Make up my sum. What wilt thou do for her?   265
King: O he is mad, Laertes.
Queen: For love of God, forbear him.
Hamlet: 'Swounds, show me what thou'lt do:
  Woul't weep? woul't fight? woul't fast? woul't tear thyself?
  Woul't drink up eisel? eat a crocodile?   270
  I'll do't. Dost thou come here to whine?
  To outface me with leaping in her grave?
  Be buried quick with her, and so will I;
  And, if thou prate of mountains, let them throw
  Millions of acres on us, till our ground,   275
  Singeing his pate against the burning Zone,
  Make Ossa like a wart! Nay, an thou'lt mouth,
  I'll rant as well as thou.
Queen: This is mere madness:
  And thus a while the fit will work on him;
  Anon, as patient as the female dove   280
  When that her golden couplets are disclosed,
  His silence will sit drooping.
Hamlet: Hear you, sir;
  What is the reason that you use me thus?

288   *Strengthen . . . speech:* Remember what we planned last
        night and be patient.

289   *present push:* immediate action

I loved you ever: but it is no matter;
Let Hercules himself do what he may,   285
The cat will mew, and dog will have his day.
                                                                    [*Exit.*]

King: I pray you, good Horatio, wait upon him.—
                                                        [*Exit Horatio.*]

[*To Laertes*]: Strengthen your patience in our last night's
    speech;
We'll put the matter to the present push.
Good Gertrude, set some watch over your son.   290
This grave shall have a living monument:
An hour of quiet shortly shall we see;
Till then, in patience our proceeding be.   [*Exeunt.*]

Act 5, Scene 1: Activities

1. The gravediggers' work is quite grim, yet their conversation is humorous. In groups, discuss why you think Shakespeare used humour at this point in the play. Are there any jobs in modern society in which people would be likely to use this kind of humour? Why do you think they might joke about their work in this way? Share your ideas with the class.

2. In line 200, Horatio replies to Hamlet's comments about death and decay by saying "'Twere to consider too curiously, to consider so." Insert a continuation of Horatio's comment, either at line 201 or at line 210. What is Horatio concerned about? Read your continuation to the class.

3. With your group, discuss the effect of Hamlet's words in lines 263–278. Do you think he is speaking the truth about his feelings for Ophelia? Present your opinion to the class.

4. In a class discussion, consider the purpose of the first part of this scene (lines 1–210). Since this play is very long, would you recommend that a director cut these lines out of a performance of the play? Be sure that you hear arguments both for and against this suggestion.

For the next scene . . .

Have you experienced a situation when you thought,
"I've done what I could, whether right or wrong. Now the
rest is up to fate"? How did you feel once you had
decided you could not do anything more? Looking
back, do you think you were right? What did you mean
by "fate"? Discuss your ideas with your group.

Act 5, Scene 2

In this scene . . .

Hamlet tells Horatio about the events on board the ship and what is in store for Rosencrantz and Guildenstern. Osric, an eccentric courtier, comes to tell Hamlet that Claudius has proposed a duel between Hamlet and Laertes. Hamlet satirizes Osric's artificial manners, but agrees to the proposal. In private, Hamlet confesses to Horatio that he has a sense of foreboding. Nevertheless, he decides to go ahead with the duel. Before the duel, Hamlet apologizes to Laertes. During the sword play, the King drops poison into a cup intended for Hamlet, but instead Gertrude drinks the poisoned wine as Claudius looks on. Laertes wounds Hamlet with a poisoned sword. Then, in a scuffle, the swords are mixed up, and Hamlet poisons Laertes with the same sword. The Queen dies, and then Laertes dies after telling Hamlet of all the treachery. Hamlet finally kills Claudius. As the play ends, Hamlet urges Horatio to live on and tell his story to the world. Meanwhile, Fortinbras approaches with his army. Just before Hamlet dies, he chooses Fortinbras as the new king. Following Fortinbras' instructions, Hamlet is carried off the stage like a soldier. Peace is restored to Denmark.

1	*So much . . . the other:* Hamlet, who has just finished one subject of discussion, is now turning to the subject of his escape at sea.
6	*mutines in the bilboes:* rebellious sailors imprisoned in iron shackles
9	*pall:* fail
10-11	*There's a divinity . . . will:* Providence (destiny) controls our lives, regardless of the efforts we make.
11	*Rough-hew:* crudely shape (as in shaping timber with an axe)
13	*scarfed:* loosely wrapped
14	*them:* Rosencrantz and Guildenstern
15	*Finger'd:* took; *in fine:* in conclusion, finally
20	*Larded:* embellished; *several:* separate
21	*Importing:* concerning
22	*With, ho! . . . my life:* with such imagined dangers (bugbears and goblins) if I continued to live
23	*on the supervise . . . bated:* immediately on reading this, without hesitation

Scene 2

A hall in the castle.
Enter Hamlet and Horatio.

Hamlet: So much for this, sir; now let me see the other;
    You do remember all the circumstance?
Horatio: Remember it, my lord!
Hamlet: Sir, in my heart there was a kind of fighting,
    That would not let me sleep: methought I lay   5
    Worse than the mutines in the bilboes. Rashly,
    And praised be rashness for it, let us know,
    Our indiscretion sometimes serves us well,
    When our dear plots do pall: and that should teach us
    There's a divinity that shapes our ends,   10
    Rough-hew them how we will.
Horatio: That is most certain.
Hamlet: Up from my cabin,
    My sea-gown scarfed about me, in the dark
    Groped I to find out them: had my desire,
    Finger'd their packet and in fine withdrew   15
    To mine own room again: making so bold,
    My fears forgetting manners, to unseal
    Their grand commission; where I found, Horatio,—
    O royal knavery!—an exact command,
    Larded with many several sorts of reasons,   20
    Importing Denmark's health and England's too,
    With, ho! such bugs and goblins in my life,
    That, on the supervise, no leisure bated,
    No, not to stay the grinding of the axe,
    My head should be struck off.
Horatio: Is it possible?   25
Hamlet: Here's the commission; read it at more leisure.
    But wilt thou hear me how I did proceed?
Horatio: I beseech you.

29	*be-netted:* ensnared
30-31	*Ere I could . . . play:* Before I consciously had time to think, my brain took over and started the action.
33	*statists:* politicians
36	*yeoman's service:* loyal service
38	*conjuration:* appeal
42	*And stand . . . amities:* and serve as a link in their friendship
43	*"Ases":* This refers to the word "as," repeated in his letter. It also suggests "asses" carrying a burden (great charge); *charge:* significance
47	*shriving-time:* time for confessing sins and receiving absolution
48	*was heaven ordinant:* heaven was guiding matters (in my favour)
49	*signet:* official seal
50	*model:* exact replica
52	*Subscribed . . . impression:* signed and sealed it (with wax)
54	*what . . . sequent:* what happened after this
56	*go to't:* go to their deaths
58	*near:* on
58-59	*their defeat . . . grow:* Their deaths were caused by their own meddling.
61	*pass:* sword thrust; *fell incensed:* fiercely angry
62	*mighty opposites:* i.e., Claudius and himself
63	*Does it not . . . upon:* Is it not my responsibility?

Hamlet: Being thus be-netted round with villainies,—
    Ere I could make a prologue to my brains, 30
    They had begun the play,—I sat me down;
    Devised a new commission; wrote it fair:
    I once did hold it, as our statists do,
    A baseness to write fair, and labour'd much
    How to forget that learning; but, sir, now 35
    It did me yeoman's service: wilt thou know
    The effects of what I wrote?
Horatio: Ay, good my lord.
Hamlet: An earnest conjuration from the king,
    As England was his faithful tributary,
    As love between them as the palm should flourish, 40
    As peace should still her wheaten garland wear,
    And stand a comma 'tween their amities,
    And many such like "Ases" of great charge,
    That, on the view and know of these contents,
    Without debatement further, more or less, 45
    He should the bearers put to sudden death.
    Not shriving-time allow'd.
Horatio: How was this seal'd?
Hamlet: Why, even in that was heaven ordinant.
    I had my father's signet in my purse,
    Which was the model of that Danish seal: 50
    Folded the writ up in form of the other;
    Subscribed it; gave't the impression; placed it safely,
    The changeling never known. Now, the next day
    Was our sea-fight: and what to this was sequent
    Thou know'st already. 55
Horatio: So Guildenstern and Rosencrantz go to't.
Hamlet: Why, man, they did make love to this
        employment;
    They are not near my conscience; their defeat
    Does by their own insinuation grow:
    'Tis dangerous when the baser nature comes 60
    Between the pass and fell incensed points
    Of mighty opposites.
Horatio: Why, what a king is this!
Hamlet: Does it not, think'st thee, stand me now upon—
    He that hath kill'd my king, and whored my mother;

66	*Thrown out . . . life:* attempted to take my own (proper) life. The image is taken from fishing (angling).
67	*cozenage:* trickery
68	*quit:* repay
69	*canker:* a spreading sore. Note the disease imagery.
70	*In:* into
73	*It:* the time (before news reaches Denmark of the deaths of Rosencrantz and Guildenstern). Note Hamlet's new resolution and confidence.
74	*And a man's . . . "One":* A man's life is barely long enough for him to say "One."
77-78	*For by . . . his:* My own cause appears the same as his.
79	*bravery:* flamboyance, bravado
82-83	*water-fly:* The water-fly, flapping its wings and skipping up and down on the water's surface, symbolizes a busybody.
86-87	*let a . . . mess:* Any rough person who has money can now be admitted to the royal court and dine at the King's table; the King himself is too crude to notice.
88	*chough:* jackdaw, a bird noted for its chattering.
93	*bonnet:* hat; *to his right use:* Osric is likely making exaggerated, sweeping gestures with his hat.
92-104	Hamlet is mocking Osric's exaggeratedly polite behaviour.

Popp'd in between the election and my hopes;   65
Thrown out his angle for my proper life,
And with such cozenage,—is't not perfect conscience,
To quit him with this arm? and is't not to be damn'd,
To let this canker of our nature come
In further evil?   70
Horatio: It must be shortly known to him from England
What is the issue of the business there.
Hamlet: It will be short: the interim is mine;
And a man's life's no more than to say, "One."
But I am very sorry, good Horatio,   75
That to Laertes I forgot myself;
For by the image of my cause, I see
The portraiture of his: I'll court his favours:
But, sure, the bravery of his grief did put me
Into a towering passion.
Horatio: Peace! who comes here?   80

[Enter Osric.]

Osric: Your lordship is right welcome back to Denmark.
Hamlet: I humbly thank you, sir. Dost know this water-
   fly?
Horatio: No, my good lord.
Hamlet: Thy state is the more gracious, for 'tis a vice to   85
   know him. He hath much land, and fertile; let a beast
   be lord of beasts, and his crib shall stand at the king's
   mess: 'tis a chough, but, as I say, spacious in the
   possession of dirt.
Osric: Sweet lord, if your lordship were at leisure, I should   90
   impart a thing to you from his majesty.
Hamlet: I will receive it with all diligence of spirit.
   Put your bonnet to his right use: 'tis for the head.
Osric: I thank your lordship, it is very hot.
Hamlet: No, believe me, 'tis very cold; the wind is   95
   northerly.
Osric: It is indifferent cold, my lord, indeed.
Hamlet: Methinks it is very sultry and hot, for my
   complexion—
Osric: Exceedingly, my lord; it is very sultry, as 'twere,—I   100
   cannot tell how. But, my lord, his majesty bade me

107	*differences:* distinctive qualities
108	*soft society:* pleasing manners
109-110	*card . . . gentry:* model of a perfect gentleman
110	*continent:* epitome

112	*his definement . . . in you:* His reputation doesn't suffer from your account of it.
112-119	Hamlet is matching Osric's affected language in describing Laertes.
113-114	*to divide . . . memory:* to try to make a list (inventory) of all his good qualities would make the memory reel
114-115	*and yet . . . sail:* and still the attempt to describe them would be slow and awkward in comparison, just as a boat rolling about heavily is surpassed by one sailing quickly
115-116	*in the verity of extolment:* to praise him truly
116	*article:* importance
117-119	*his infusion . . . more:* His qualities are of such value and rarity that, to speak truly of him, nothing is like him except his own reflection; anyone who tries to imitate him is no better than his shadow.
121	*The concernancy, sir?:* What is the point, sir? Hamlet is wondering why they are discussing Laertes.
122	*more rawer breath:* cruder language
124-125	*Is't not possible . . . really:* Can you not understand your own language when someone else speaks it? You will be able to if you try.
126	*What imports . . . gentleman?:* Why are you mentioning this gentleman?
133	*approve:* commend
135-137	*I dare . . . himself:* I do not dare agree with that because I will seem to be comparing my excellence with his; yet, one can only know another person if one knows oneself well first.
138	*weapon:* style of fencing
138-139	*but in the imputation . . . unfellowed:* The people in his service say his reputation is unequalled.

signify to you that he has laid a great wager on your
head: sir, this is the matter—
Hamlet: I beseech you, remember—
                    [*Hamlet moves him to put on his hat.*]
Osric: Nay, good my lord; for mine ease, in good faith, Sir,   105
here is newly come to court, Laertes: believe me, an
absolute gentleman, full of most excellent differences,
of very soft society and great showing: indeed, to
speak feelingly of him, he is the card or calendar of
gentry, for you shall find in him the continent of what   110
part a gentleman would see.
Hamlet: Sir, his definement suffers no perdition in you;
though, I know, to divide him inventorially would dizzy
the arithmetic of memory, and yet but yaw neither,
in respect of his quick sail. But in the verity of   115
extolment, I take him to be a soul of great article, and
his infusion of such dearth and rareness, as, to make
true diction of him, his semblable is his mirror, and who
else would trace him, his umbrage, nothing more.
Osric: Your lordship speaks most infallibly of him.   120
Hamlet: The concernancy, sir? why do we wrap the
gentleman in our more rawer breath?
Osric: Sir?
Horatio: Is't not possible to understand in another tongue?
You will do't, sir, really.   125
Hamlet: What imports the nomination of this gentleman?
Osric: Of Laertes?
Horatio: His purse is empty already; all his golden words
are spent.
Hamlet: Of him, sir.   130
Osric: I know you are not ignorant—
Hamlet: I would, you did, sir; yet, in faith, if you did, it
would not much approve me. Well, sir?
Osric: You are not ignorant of what excellence Laertes is—
Hamlet: I dare not confess that, lest I should compare with   135
him in excellence; but, to know a man well, were to
know himself.
Osric: I mean, sir, for his weapon; but in the imputation
laid on him by them, in his meed he's unfellowed.
Hamlet: What's his weapon?   140

143-144   *Barbary horses:* a North African breed, famous for their speed

144   *imponed:* bet, wagered

145   *poniards:* daggers; *assigns:* accessories

146   *girdle:* sword belt; *hanger:* the straps that held the sword to the girdle

148   *of very liberal conceit:* richly ornamented

150   *edified by the margent:* instructed by explanatory notes (receive an explanation from notes in the margin)

153   *germane:* relevant

160   *laid:* bet, wagered

160-162   *The king . . . nine:* The King is allowing Hamlet a handicap. Laertes must win three bouts more than Hamlet in a total of twelve bouts.

163-164   *vouchsafe the answer:* accept the challenge

169   *breathing time of day:* time for exercise

170   *foils:* blunted rapiers used for fencing

174   *re-deliver you:* deliver your message

180   *This lapwing . . . head:* The shell probably refers to Osric's ornate hat. According to a popular proverb, the lapwing represented a pretentious young person, since it leaves its nest a few hours after birth.

Osric: Rapier and dagger.

Hamlet: That's two of his weapons: but, well.

Osric: The king, sir, hath waged with him six Barbary
     horses: against the which he has imponed, as I take it,
     six French rapiers and poniards, with their assigns,   145
     as girdle, hanger, and so: three of the carriages, in faith,
     are very dear to fancy, very responsive to the hilts,
     most delicate carriages, and of very liberal conceit.

Hamlet: What call you the carriages?

Horatio: I knew you must be edified by the margent ere   150
     you had done.

Osric: The carriages, sir, are the hangers.

Hamlet: The phrase would be more germane to the matter
     if we could carry cannon by our sides: I would it
     might be hangers till then. But on: six Barbary horses   155
     against six French swords, their assigns, and three
     liberal-conceited carriages: that's the French bet
     against the Danish. Why is this "imponed," as you
     call it?

Osric: The king, sir, hath laid, that in a dozen passes between   160
     you and him, he shall not exceed you three hits; he
     hath laid on twelve for nine; and it would come to
     immediate trial, if your lordship would vouchsafe
     the answer.

Hamlet: How if I answer "No"?   165

Osric: I mean, my lord, the opposition of your person in
     trial.

Hamlet: Sir, I will walk here in the hall; if it please his
     majesty, it is the breathing time of day with me: let
     the foils be brought, the gentleman willing, and the   170
     king hold his purpose, I will win for him an I can; if
     not, I will gain nothing but my shame and the odd
     hits.

Osric: Shall I re-deliver you e'en so?

Hamlet: To this effect, sir, after what flourish your nature   175
     will.

Osric: I commend my duty to your lordship.

Hamlet: Yours, yours. [*Exit Osric.*] He does well to commend
     it himself: there are no tongues else for's turn.

Horatio: This lapwing runs away with the shell on his head.   180

181	*He did comply . . . it:* He observed the formalities of polite social behaviour before he would suckle.
183	*drossy:* silly
183-184	*tune of the time:* superficial fashion; *outward habit of encounter:* the outward style of conversation
184-187	*a kind . . . are out:* Hamlet is using an image from breweries. Ultimately, these courtiers, are as empty as beer bubbles.
185	*yesty:* frothy
186	*fond:* foolish; *winnowed:* flimsy
188	*commended:* sent his respects
189	*attend:* wait for
193-194	*if his fitness . . . ready:* If he (Laertes) is ready, so am I.
196	*In happy time:* at an appropriate time
197-198	*use some . . . Laertes:* show some politeness
203	*how ill . . . heart:* Hamlet has a feeling something will go wrong.
206	*gain giving:* feeling of anxiety, misgiving
208-209	*forestall their repair:* prevent them from coming
210	*we defy augury:* I don't pay attention to superstitious prophecies.
210-211	*there's a special . . . sparrow:* This is a reference to the Bible (Matthew 10:29). "Are not two sparrows sold for a copper coin? And not one of them falls to the ground without your Father's will." Belief in fate and predestination was popular in Shakespeare's time.
211	*it:* death
213	*the readiness:* i.e., the readiness to accept one's fate, to die
213-215	*Since no man . . . betimes?:* Hamlet seems to be accepting the idea that he will never gain complete understanding of life.
214	*aught:* anything
215	*betimes:* early

Hamlet: He did comply with his dug before he sucked it.
    Thus has he—and many more of the same breed that
    I know the drossy age dotes on—only got the tune of
    the time, and outward habit of encounter; a kind of
    yesty collection, which carries them through and   185
    through the most fond and winnowed opinions; and
    do but blow them to their trial, the bubbles are out.

  [Enter a Lord.]

Lord: My lord, his majesty commended him to you by young
    Osric, who brings back to him, that you attend him
    in the hall: he sends to know if your pleasure hold to   190
    play with Laertes, or that you will take longer time.
Hamlet: I am constant to my purposes; they follow the king's
    pleasure: if his fitness speaks, mine is ready; now or
    whensoever, provided I be so able as now.
Lord: The king and queen and all are coming down.   195
Hamlet: In happy time.
Lord: The queen desires you to use some gentle
    entertainment to Laertes before you fall to play.
Hamlet: She well instructs me.   *[Exit Lord.]*
Horatio: You will lose this wager, my lord.   200
Hamlet: I do not think so; since he went into France, I have
    been in continual practice; I shall win at the odds. But
    thou wouldst not think how ill all's here about my heart:
    but it is no matter.
Horatio: Nay, good my lord—   205
Hamlet: It is but foolery; but it is such a kind of gain giving,
    as would perhaps trouble a woman.
Horatio: If your mind dislike anything, obey it. I will forestall
    their repair hither, and say you are not fit.
Hamlet: Not a whit; we defy augury: there's a special   210
    providence in the fall of a sparrow. If it be now, 'tis
    not to come; if it be not to come, it will be now; if it
    be not now, yet it will come: the readiness is all: since
    no man has aught of what he leaves, what is't to leave
    betimes? Let be.   215

  [Enter King, Queen, Laertes, and Lords, Osric, and
  Attendants with foils. A table with flagons of wine on it.]

219	*This presence:* those who are present
222	*nature:* your natural feelings (as a son whose father has been killed); *exception:* your sense of being wronged
223-230	*I here proclaim madness . . . enemy:* Hamlet seems to be admitting that he really *was* mad. He admits that there were times when he temporarily lost control of his mind.
225	*If Hamlet from himself be ta'en away:* This idea reflects modern descriptions of madness: "He's beside himself." "She's not all there."
232	*purposed:* deliberate
235	*in nature:* with regard to my duty as a son
237	*in my terms of honour:* in matters affecting my honour
237-240	Even if Laertes forgives Hamlet personally, he is still obliged to defend his honour officially.
240	*a voice . . . peace:* an authoritative judgment as grounds for making peace
241	*name ungored:* reputation undamaged
246	*foil:* the setting of a jewel, which shows the stone at its best; also, a sword
248	*Stick fiery off:* stand out in brilliant contrast

King: Come, Hamlet, come, and take this hand from me.
      [*The King puts the hand of Laertes into that of Hamlet.*]
Hamlet: Give me your pardon, sir; I have done you wrong;
   But pardon't, as you are a gentleman.
   This presence knows, and you must needs have heard,
   How I am punish'd with a sore distraction.   220
   What I have done,
   That might your nature, honour, and exception
   Roughly awake, I here proclaim was madness.
   Was't Hamlet wrong'd Laertes? Never Hamlet:
   If Hamlet from himself be ta'en away,   225
   And when he's not himself does wrong Laertes,
   Then Hamlet does it not, Hamlet denies it.
   Who does it then? His madness: if't be so,
   Hamlet is of the faction that is wrong'd;
   His madness is poor Hamlet's enemy.   230
   Sir, in this audience,
   Let my disclaiming from a purposed evil
   Free me so far in your most generous thoughts,
   That I have shot mine arrow o'er the house,
   And hurt my brother.
Laertes: I am satisfied in nature,   235
   Whose motive, in this case, should stir me most
   To my revenge: but in my terms of honour
   I stand aloof, and will no reconcilement,
   Till by some elder masters, of known honour,
   I have a voice and precedent of peace,   240
   To keep my name ungored. But till that time,
   I do receive your offer'd love like love
   And will not wrong it.
Hamlet: I embrace it freely,
   And will this brother's wager frankly play.
   Give us the foils. Come on.
Laertes: Come, one for me.   245
Hamlet: I'll be your foil, Laertes; in mine ignorance
   Your skill shall, like a star i' the darkest night,
   Stick fiery off indeed.
Laertes: You mock me, sir.
Hamlet: No, by this hand.
King: Give them the foils, young Osric. Cousin Hamlet,   250

254   *since he's better'd:* since Laertes is considered the better swordsman

256   *This likes me well:* This pleases me.

260   *quit . . . exchange:* reach a tie in the third bout

261   *ordnance:* cannon

262   *better breath:* improved strength

263   *union:* a pearl

266   *kettle:* kettledrum

273   *this pearl is thine:* Claudius drops the pearl (and, thus, the poison) into Hamlet's wine cup.

280   *napkin:* handkerchief

281   *carouses to thy fortune:* drinks to your health

You know the wager?
Hamlet: Very well, my lord;
   Your grace hath laid the odds o' the weaker side.
King: I do not fear it; I have seen you both:
   But since he's better'd, we have therefore odds.
Laertes: This is too heavy, let me see another.   255
Hamlet: This likes me well: these foils have all a length?
                     [*They prepare to play.*]
Osric: Ay, my good lord.
King: Set me the stoups of wine upon that table.
   If Hamlet give the first or second hit,
   Or quit in answer of the third exchange,   260
   Let all the battlements their ordnance fire;
   The king shall drink to Hamlet's better breath;
   And in the cup an union shall he throw,
   Richer than that which four successive kings
   In Denmark's crown have worn. Give me the cups;   265
   And let the kettle to the trumpet speak,
   The trumpet to the cannonier without,
   The cannons to the heavens, the heaven to earth,
   Now the king drinks to Hamlet. Come, begin;
   And you, the judges, bear a wary eye.   270
Hamlet: Come on, sir.
Laertes: Come, my lord.   [*They play.*]
Hamlet: One.
Laertes: No.
Hamlet: Judgment.
Osric: A hit, a very palpable hit.
Laertes: Well; again.
King: Stay; give me drink. Hamlet, this pearl is thine;
   Here's to thy health.
         [*Trumpets sound; and cannons shot off within.*]
   Give him the cup.   275
Hamlet: I'll play this bout first; set it by awhile.
   Come. [*They play.*] Another hit; what say you?
Laertes: A touch, a touch, I do confess.
King: Our son shall win.
Queen: He's fat, and scant of breath.
   Here, Hamlet, take my napkin, rub thy brows: 280
   The queen carouses to thy fortune, Hamlet.

291   *you make a wanton of me:* you are not taking me seriously

297   *They bleed on both sides!:* They have both been wounded.

299   *as a woodcock to mine own springe:* like a bird caught in my own trap

301   *swounds:* faints

310   *practice:* scheme

Hamlet: Good, madam!
King: Gertrude, do not drink.
Queen: I will, my lord; I pray you pardon me.
King [Aside]: It is the poison'd cup: it is too late.
Hamlet: I dare not drink yet, madam; by and by.   285
Queen: Come, let me wipe thy face.
Laertes: My lord, I'll hit him now.
King: I do not think't.
Laertes [Aside]: And yet it is almost against my conscience.
Hamlet: Come, for the third, Laertes: you but dally;
   I pray you, pass with your best violence;   290
   I am afeard you make a wanton of me.
Laertes: Say you so? come on.   [*They play.*]
Osric: Nothing, neither way.
Laertes: Have at you now.
     [*Laertes wounds Hamlet; then, in scuffling, they change
           rapiers, and Hamlet wounds Laertes.*]
King: Part them; they are incensed.   295
Hamlet: Nay, come again.   [*The Queen falls.*]
Osric: Look to the queen there, ho!
Horatio: They bleed on both sides! How is it, my lord?
Osric: How is't Laertes?
Laertes: Why, as a woodcock to mine own springe, Osric;
   I am justly kill'd with mine own treachery.   300
Hamlet: How does the queen?
King: She swounds to see them bleed.
Queen: No, no, the drink, the drink!—O my dear
    Hamlet!—
   The drink, the drink! I am poison'd!   [*Dies.*]
Hamlet: O villainy! Ho! let the door be lock'd:
   Treachery! seek it out.   [*Laertes falls.*]   305
Laertes: It is here, Hamlet: Hamlet, thou art slain:
   No medicine in the world can do thee good,
   In thee there is not half an hour of life;
   The treacherous instrument is in thy hand,
   Unbated and envenom'd: the foul practice   310
   Hath turn'd itself on me; lo, here I lie,
   Never to rise again: thy mother's poison'd:
   I can no more: the king, the king's to blame.
Hamlet: The point envenom'd too!

319   *union:* a pun. Hamlet is referring to the pearl Claudius put in the cup and to the fact that now Claudius will join Gertrude in death.

321   *temper'd:* prepared

326   *I am dead:* I am certain to die.

327   *chance:* event

328   *mutes:* actors without speaking parts

329   *fell:* cruel; *sergeant:* Death is personified as an officer summoning Hamlet into his custody.

332-333   *report . . . unsatisfied:* Clear my name with those who do not understand why I behaved as I did.

334   *I am more . . . Dane:* Famous Romans committed suicide instead of accepting defeat.

340   *Absent thee from felicity awhile:* Forgo that happiness for a while.

346   *o'ercrows:* triumphs over (as a cock crows in triumph)

Then, venom, to thy work.   [*Stabs the King.*]   315
All: Treason! treason!
King: O, yet defend me, friends: I am but hurt.
Hamlet: Here, thou incestuous, murderous, damned
    Dane, Drink off this potion. Is thy union here?
    Follow my mother.   [*King dies.*]
Laertes: He is justly served;   320
    It is a poison temper'd by himself.
    Exchange forgiveness with me, noble Hamlet:
    Mine and my father's death come not upon thee.
    Nor thine on me!   [*Dies.*]
Hamlet: Heaven make thee free of it! I follow thee.   325
    I am dead, Horatio. Wretched queen, adieu!
    You that look pale and tremble at this chance,
    That are but mutes or audience to this act,
    Had I but time—as this fell sergeant, death,
    Is strict in his arrest—O, I could tell you,—   330
    But let it be. Horatio, I am dead;
    Thou livest; report me and my cause aright
    To the unsatisfied.
Horatio: Never believe it:
    I am more an antique Roman than a Dane:
    Here's yet some liquor left.
Hamlet: As thou'rt a man,   335
    Give me the cup: let go; by heaven I'll have it.
    O good Horatio, what a wounded name,
    Things standing thus unknown, shall live behind me!
    If thou didst ever hold me in thy heart,
    Absent thee from felicity a while,   340
    And in this harsh world draw thy breath in pain,
    To tell my story.   [*March afar off, and shot without.*]
        What warlike noise is this?

Osric: Young Fortinbras, with conquest come from
        Poland,
    To the ambassadors of England gives
    This warlike volley.
Hamlet: O, I die, Horatio;   345
    The potent poison quite o'ercrows my spirit;
    I cannot live to hear the news from England;

348-349 *the election lights . . . voice:* Hamlet gives his approval to Fortinbras as Denmark's new king.

350-351 *the occurrents . . . solicited:* The events, great and small, that have led to this moment.

357 *This quarry cries on havoc:* This pile of dead bodies indicates a terrible slaughter.

357-360 *O proud . . . struck?:* Once again, death is personified. Here, death is compared to a hunter who will devour his prey (quarry).

358 *What feast . . . cell:* What feast is being prepared in the grave?

360 *dismal:* dreadful

365 *his:* Claudius'

368 *jump upon this bloody question:* at the precise moment of this bloody event

374 *carnal, bloody, and unnatural acts:* Claudius' sins

375 *accidental judgments:* Ophelia's death, and perhaps Gertrude's as well; *casual slaughters:* the murder of Polonius

376 *deaths put on by cunning:* Rosencrantz and Guildenstern's deaths, and perhaps Hamlet's death too

377-378 *purposes . . . heads:* the deaths of Laertes and Claudius

379 *deliver:* report

But I do prophesy the election lights
On Fortinbras; he has my dying voice;
So tell him, with the occurrents, more and less,   350
Which have solicited. The rest is silence.   [*Dies.*]
Horatio: Now cracks a noble heart. Good night, sweet
    prince,
And flights of angels sing thee to thy rest!
[March within.]
Why does the drum come hither?

[*Enter Fortinbras, the English Ambassadors and others.*]

Fortinbras: Where is this sight?
Horatio: What is it ye would see?   355
If aught of woe or wonder, cease your search.
Fortinbras: This quarry cries on havoc. O proud death,
What feast is toward in thine eternal cell,
That thou so many princes at a shot
So bloodily hast struck?
First Ambassador: The sight is dismal;   360
And our affairs from England come too late:
The ears are senseless that should give us hearing,
To tell him, his commandment is fulfill'd,
That Rosencrantz and Guildenstern are dead:
Where should we have our thanks?
Horatio: Not from his mouth   365
Had it the ability of life to thank you:
He never gave commandment for their death.
But since, so jump upon this bloody question,
You from the Polack wars, and you from England,
Are here arrived, give order that these bodies   370
High on a stage be placed to the view;
And let me speak, to the yet unknowing world
How these things came about: so shall you hear
Of carnal, bloody, and unnatural acts,
Of accidental judgments, casual slaughters,   375
Of deaths put on by cunning and forced cause,
And, in this upshot, purposes mistook
Fall'n on the inventors' heads: all this can I
Truly deliver.
Fortinbras: Let us haste to hear it,

And call the noblest to the audience. 380
For me, with sorrow I embrace my fortune;
I have some rights of memory in this kingdom,
Which now to claim my vantage doth invite me.
Horatio: Of that I shall have also cause to speak,
And from his mouth whose voice will draw on more: 385
But let this same be presently perform'd.
Even while men's minds are wild; lest more mischance
On plots and errors happen.
Fortinbras: Let four captains
Bear Hamlet, like a soldier, to the stage;
For he was likely, had he been put on, 390
To have proved most royally: and, for his passage,
The soldiers' music and the rites of war
Speak loudly for him.
Take up the bodies: such a sight as this
Becomes the field, but here shows much amiss. 395
Go, bid the soldiers shoot.
> [*A dead march. Exeunt, bearing off the bodies: after
> which a peal of ordnance is shot off.*]

Act 5, Scene 2: Activities

1. Do you think Rosencrantz and Guildenstern deserved to be put to death? In your group, discuss what alternative actions Hamlet might have taken. Examine Hamlet's reasoning (lines 57–62) and consider whether you think Hamlet was seeking justice or revenge.

2. Create an official announcement to be read at a meeting of all the lords and ladies of the court, giving details about the upcoming duel between Laertes and Hamlet. If you wish, you could prepare the announcement on a computer, using appropriate fonts.

3. In the role of Hamlet, who has already experienced a premonition of death (line 203), write a letter to Gertrude, expressing your final thoughts to her. Share the letter with the class.

4. Even though Hamlet knows that Claudius has plotted his murder, he consents to participate in a duel that Claudius organized. Discuss with the class why Hamlet is eager to have the duel.

5. Personification is a figure of speech in which a thing or an idea is represented as a person or as having human characteristics. In this scene, death is personified twice—first as a police officer by Hamlet (line 329), and then as a hunter by Fortinbras (lines 357–359). In your group, discuss why you think death is pictured as having these two particular occupations.

6. Suppose that you are Fortinbras, taking over the kingdom of Denmark. Write a list of things you will do to restore order and win the confidence of the Danish people.

7. Just before Hamlet dies, he says to Horatio,

   > If thou didst ever hold me in thy heart,
   > Absent thee from felicity a while,
   > And in this harsh world draw thy breath in pain,
   > To tell my story. (lines 339–342)

In about two hundred words, write a letter from Horatio to Hamlet's friends in Wittenberg, with the aim of helping them understand the shocking news of their friend Hamlet's death.

8. Divide the class into four groups. Each group should consider the last thoughts of one of the following: Gertrude, Claudius, Laertes, Hamlet. In your group, create a collage from magazine photos or art that represents this character's thoughts. Display the collages.

Consider the Whole Play

1. Choose a character who dies during the course of the play. Write a monologue that the character might deliver if he or she came back from the dead. The monologue should be consistent with the portrayal of the character in the play. The character could confess or reveal things that were unknown when they were alive. This could include things that they themselves did not realize while they were still living. Present the monologues live or on videotape to the class. (Before beginning to write the monologue, discuss your ideas with others in the class who have chosen the same character.)

2. Prepare a radio news report (up to two minutes long) covering:

   - a description of the location

   - a description of the crowd—its size and its mood

   - an account of Fortinbras' background and personal qualities

   - highlights of Fortinbras' coronation speech (and the crowd's response)

   - a summary of the events in Elsinore, starting with the death of old King Hamlet, that led to Fortinbras' accession to the throne

   - a closing comment on the future of Denmark

   Tape your report and play it for the class. You may wish to listen to some radio news reports as you plan your own report.

3. Actors often appear on television talk shows to attract a wider audience for a new play or film. With your group, stage a talk show interview featuring one or two actors who will be playing major roles in an upcoming production of *Hamlet*. Your purpose is to arouse the interest of people who are not familiar with the play and who might shy away from a Shakespearean production. Videotape this interview for the class.

4. As an actor, you must choose to audition for the role of Gertrude, Ophelia, Claudius, Polonius, Laertes, or Horatio. Which role would you choose? Write a letter to the director, giving your concept of the character and explaining why you would suit the role.

5. Design a full-page newspaper advertisement for a theatre production of *Hamlet*. Your advertisement should contain a strong visual element and words that attract readers to the play. The advertisement should also provide information about the location, dates, and times of the performance, as well as prices of the tickets.

6. Present Hamlet's complex mind as a collage. Demonstrate your own understanding of his character by your choice and positioning of images.

7. Prepare a talk for the class about how women are presented in the play. From reviews of past productions of *Hamlet* in the library or on the Internet, find out about different ways these female roles have been interpreted. Make some suggestions about how the interpretation of Ophelia's and Gertrude's characters could be updated to be more in tune with women's roles today.

8. Research the production of *Hamlet* that you have been watching on video or DVD in class or a different production. (Three well-known contemporary productions feature Kenneth Branagh, Mel Gibson, and Derek Jacobi as Hamlet.) Using the Internet, find interviews with the main actors, reviews of the production, photographs, and comparisons with other productions. Present your findings in the form of an essay or a report to the class.

9. Directors of *Hamlet* often choose to place the play in a specific historical or social setting, often as a way of commenting on the play. Choose one of the following settings, then research the time period and create a portfolio of clothing, furniture, architecture, and interior decor for a director to use:

   • an unnamed European country in the early 1940s, amid the tension of war
   • a medieval castle

- a fast-paced, modern corporate setting
- the music industry or Hollywood
- another time period or setting of your choice

10. For each of the main characters in the play, find a suitable computer font. Create a small poster featuring an important quotation from each character, in the font you have chosen. Comment on the suitability of the font for each character.

11. In your group, create storyboards for a 30-second television commercial for a production of *Hamlet*. Your purpose is to create an intriguing atmosphere about the play, and to provide information that will attract an audience.

12. You have been commissioned to design a Hamlet Memorial Park in Elsinore, Denmark. In this modern park, how will you reflect the story of Hamlet and his personality? Choose one of the following activities:

- Create a portfolio of drawings and text that explain your plan.
- Create a tourist brochure advertising this park, with a map of its main features.

13. Write a series of "Companions Wanted" ads for Gertrude, Claudius, the old King Hamlet, Hamlet, Polonius, and Ophelia. Each ad should include a description of the person, then a description of his or her ideal partner. Consult the "Personals" column in newspapers for ideas.

14. Prepare an activity for the class where you show a key scene from *Hamlet* from two different video or DVD productions. Because you will be familiar with the scenes, you can ask the class questions that highlight the differences between the two versions. Invite students to state their preferences.

15. The play *Hamlet* reflects many Elizabethan ideas about life and the universe. Using resource material about Elizabethan England (or Renaissance England), research one or more of the following concepts: the four humours, the four elements, melancholy, reason and passion, love,

sin, art, male and female characteristics. Present your insights in a formal essay or a class presentation that shows the ways in which these ideas are present in *Hamlet*.

16. Ophelia—especially her death—has been a subject for visual artists through the centuries. Research the portrayal of Ophelia by different artists and write an essay about your impressions. (You can find material by searching the Internet.) Include your own ideas about how Ophelia could be portrayed in the visual arts today.

17. Write an essay in which you consider the relationship between revenge and justice. In your argument, you might allude to Hamlet or to current events.

18. Create a poster that advertises an upcoming production of *Hamlet*. The poster should contain one strong dominant image that you feel represents the play.